INTERNATIONAL SERIES OF MONOGRAPHS ON
ANALYTICAL CHEMISTRY

GENERAL EDITORS: R. BELCHER AND L. GORDON

Volume 15

OTHER TITLES IN THE SERIES ON ANALYTICAL CHEMISTRY

INORGANIC ULTRAMICROANALYSIS

INORGANIC ULTRAMICROANALYSIS

BY

I. P. ALIMARIN

AND

M. N. PETRIKOVA

TRANSLATED BY
M. G. HELL

A Pergamon Press Book

THE MACMILLAN COMPANY

NEW YORK

1964

96658

544.8
A 411

THE MACMILLAN COMPANY
60 Fifth Avenue
New York 11, N.Y.

This book is distributed by
THE MACMILLAN COMPANY
pursuant to a special arrangement with
PERGAMON PRESS LIMITED
Oxford, England

Copyright © 1964
PERGAMON PRESS LTD.

Library of Congress Catalog Card Number 63–11924

This translation has been made from I. P. Alimarin's
and M. N. Petrikova's book entitled *Neorganicheskii
ul'tramikroanaliz*, published in Moscow 1960 by the
Academy of Sciences

Set in 10 *on* 12*pt Times and Printed in Great Britain by*
THE PITMAN PRESS, BATH

CONTENTS

vii

PREFACE

ULTRAMICROANALYSIS is a comparatively new technique in analytical chemistry which provides a solution to the problem of analysing very small samples of any nature and composition.

The method permits work with small quantities of a substance (10^{-6} to 10^{-12} g) whilst maintaining the normal concentrations of the solutes; this last condition is realized by the use of small volumes (10^{-3} to 10^{-6} ml), which require special experimental techniques. Because the same conditions hold as in normal determinations, ultramicroanalysis is founded on the same principles as macroanalysis. The familiar chemical and physico-chemical methods of analysis may, therefore, be used here too, the apparatus and techniques being modified as necessary to suit work with small volumes. In this connexion, the present monograph contains, essentially, a description of the technique and experimental method used on the ultramicroscale.

It should be remarked that, initially, ultramicroanalysis was used principally in biochemistry in the study of the vital processes of cells. Thereafter the technique and experimental procedures began to be used in other spheres of natural science as well. Ultramicroanalysis was developed specially in connexion with the solution of the problems of radiochemistry and the study of the properties of the synthetic radioactive elements, which were obtained initially only in very small quantities.

In the present work the authors' many years of experience in this sphere are summarized, and a number of new methods are described which have been subjected to practical tests in the V. I. Vernadskii Institute for Geochemistry and Analytical Chemistry of the Academy of Sciences of the U.S.S.R.

Further, the book includes the work of other scientists, as far as could be gathered from the literature.

The authors do not claim to offer a thorough exposition of the subject or an exhaustive bibliography. The purpose of this little book is, above all, to help the analytical chemist to acquire the experimental technique of ultramicroanalysis for work on the microscope stage with the aid of micromanipulators. The authors hope that inorganic ultramicroanalysis will soon find wider application both in research and in teaching laboratories.

We shall be grateful to our readers for all observations or necessary improvements that may appear in the course of practical ultramicroanalysis.

I. P. ALIMARIN
M. N. PETRIKOVA

EDITORS' PREFACE

ULTRAMICRO methods (sometimes called submicro or microgram methods) have been developed mainly during the post-war period. Their development bears a close resemblance to that of micro-analytical methods, because in both cases the technique of inorganic analysis was established long before that of organic analysis. Indeed, although ultramicro inorganic analysis can now be considered as being completely established as a general technique, several problems remain to be solved before organic ultramicroanalysis can be considered as being on a similar footing.

Inorganic ultramicroanalysis has been used to solve several important problems. The pigments used to decorate Chinese oracle bones have been analysed successfully, yet later, even a microscopic examination failed to show a sample had been taken for analysis. In the pioneer work on the transuranic elements, the chemistry of the new elements was established by this new technique. Inclusions in meteorites, coatings, corrosion products and impurities in large samples have also been analysed successfully.

The first investigator to study general methods for handling these minute quantities of sample was Benedetti-Pichler. Further contributions have been made by several groups of later investigators, notably by El-Badry and Wilson, in this country. The most recent studies have been made by Alimarin and Petrikova, working in the U.S.S.R., who have extended the technique and eliminated sources of error, hitherto overlooked. In particular, these investigators have developed chromatographic and electrochemical separation methods, and physico-chemical methods for detection of end-points.

Undoubtedly, this technique should aid in the solution of many and varied problems. This book is therefore to be welcomed as a means of placing details of the technique at the disposal of English-speaking chemists. Professor Alimarin—the senior author—has a profound knowledge of all branches of analytical chemistry. His contributions in this particular field are widely recognized and enhance the authoritative nature of this monograph.

INTRODUCTION

ULTRAMICROANALYSIS consists of a combination of working procedures and specific apparatus necessary for carrying out chemical experiments with small quantities of substances and small volumes of fluids.*

The method is used in the investigation of the composition of corrosion products, incrustations, deposits, in the analysis of inclusions in minerals, meteorites, alloys, of small volumes of fluids in biochemical researches, in the study of the chemical properties of the new elements in the early stages of their production, and, in general, in all cases when the small size of the samples precludes the use of other methods of analysis. Ultramicroanalysis may also be used to analyse the concentrate of impurities (see p. 83). The foundations of ultramicromethods of chemical analysis, their uses and the lines of further development are discussed comparatively frequently in the literature [2–10], a fact which may be attributed to the novelty of this method.

In work with small quantities of a substance it is convenient to use the units of measurement shown in Table 1 (first line given for comparison). Depending on the size of the sample to be studied, ultramicromethods have developed in two directions, which are definitive for the working technique.

On the one hand, for the manipulation of small samples (volumes of the order of 10^{-3} μl.) simple mechanical devices are used, and the majority of the chemical operations are watched by the unaided eye or with a magnifying glass.

On the other hand, in work with volumes smaller than 10^{-3} μl., all the fundamental chemical operations are performed on the microscope stage, with the simultaneous use of various kinds of micromanipulators.

The experimental technique required for the first of these has

* A detailed review of the literature on ultramicroanalysis is given in the article by Alimarin and Petrikova [1].

xiii

been developed fully and exhaustively by Korenman [11, 12] and Kirk [14].

Other workers have developed and somewhat modified the techniques, principally in the analysis of biological matter, and also for various determinations by volumetric and colorimetric methods. The last five years have seen a number of such studies [11–32].

Less attention has been devoted to the use of the microscope and manipulators, although this field of ultramicroanalysis is most

TABLE 1. UNITS OF MEASUREMENT

	Length		Mass		Volume			
					Referred to the kilogram		Referred to the decimetre	
10^0	Metre	m	Gramme	g	Litre	l.	Decimetre cubed	d^3
10^{-6}	Micron	μ	Gamma	γ	Lambda	λ	Millimetre cubed	mm^3
			Microgram	μg	Microlitre	μl		
10^{-9}	Millimicron	$m\mu$	Milligamma	$m\gamma$	Millilambda	$m\lambda$		
	Nanometre	nm	Nanogram	ng	Nanolitre	nl		

interesting, because this technique permits a very great reduction in the quantity of the substance to be analysed.

The apparatus and methods of working on the microscope stage with the aid of manipulators came into use in their most general form thanks to the work of Benedetti-Pichler and his colleagues [33–38]. Then El-Badry and Wilson [39], acknowledging Benedetti-Pichler's priority, also described the general apparatus for work on the stage with some modifications in a number of cases. In subsequent communications these authors proposed a qualitative and a semi-quantitative method of determining certain cations taking into account the special features of ultramicroanalysis [39–43]. The further development of the techniques of experimentation in the second direction has been the subject of work by Alimarin and Petrikova, a part of which has been published [44–46]. An interesting study of ionophoresis under the microscope has recently been made by Turner [47].

The present monograph is an attempt to systematize the information on the techniques of ultramicroanalysis, which is at present scattered throughout the literature.

CHAPTER I

SPECIAL FEATURES OF THE ULTRAMICROMETHOD OF CHEMICAL ANALYSIS

CHEMICAL reactions in which a small number of molecules participate differ in no way from reactions involving large quantities of a substance, provided that the number of molecules reacting statistically ensures the establishment of chemical equilibrium. This is the origin of the requirement that the concentrations of the normal method shall be conserved, which is achieved in the study of small quantities by reduction of volume [48].

Using the law of errors, as determined by the statistical conditions, and supposing that we may allow an error of 10 per cent for a qualitative detection and of 0·1 per cent for a quantitative determination, we may calculate the limiting quantity of a substance necessary for the performance of chemical operations.

$$100 \, \frac{\sqrt{n}}{n} = \text{the error in per cent} \tag{1}$$

where n is the number of reacting molecules. For a qualitative detection, taking the mean molecular weight to be equal to 60, we have:

$$10^4 \times \frac{1}{n} = 10^2, \quad \text{whence} \quad n = 100 \text{ molecules}$$

i.e. $$\frac{60 \times 100}{6 \times 10^{23}} = 10^{-20} \text{ g.}$$

For a quantitative determination, taking the same mean molecular weight, we have:

$$10^4 \times \frac{1}{n} = 10^{-2}, \quad \text{whence} \quad n = 10^6 \text{ molecules}$$

i.e. $$\frac{60 \times 10^6}{6 \times 10^{23}} = 10^{-16} \text{ g.}$$

2

With quantities of a substance exceeding this limit, any chemical operation can be performed, the degree to which the limit is exceeded depending principally on the level of development of the experimental technique and the methods of observation. Thus, for example, physico-chemical methods of registering reaction products permit a considerably greater degree of reduction in the quantity needed for analysis than visual methods (this refers especially to volumetric and colorimetric determinations). The introduction of the electron microscope [49–53] opens new vistas, leading closer than heretofore, to the analysis of the limiting quantity that still ensures the establishment of chemical equilibrium.

The maintenance of the normal concentrations of reacting substances in ultramicroanalysis, by a corresponding reduction in mass and volume leads to an increase (by comparison with the macromethod) in the relative surface area of the solution and the containing vessel, i.e., to an increase in the surface area of unit volume. This last is explained by the fact that the surface area is reduced by a smaller power than the volume. This is illustrated in Table 2 below.

TABLE 2. COMPARISON OF THE SURFACE AREA OF UNIT VOLUME IN THE MACRO- AND ULTRAMICROMETHODS

Method	Diameter of vessel, cm	Height of vessel, cm	Surface area of vessel, cm^2	Volume of solution, cm^3	Surface area of unit volume, S_{rel}	$\dfrac{S_{rel-u}}{S_{rel-m}}$
Macromethod (m)	4·0	4·0	62·5	50·0	1·25	>20
Ultramicromethod (u)	0·2	0·2	0·16	0·006	26·6	

With this relatively greater area of contact with the walls of the containing vessels, solutes are adsorbed on them and also act on the material of the walls to a significantly greater extent than in macroanalysis. In consequence, we find on the one hand loss of part of the substance under investigation and, on the other, contamination of the substance.

It should also be borne in mind that, in ultramicroanalysis, small quantities of a substance that initially occupy a large volume must be concentrated so that the appropriate technique can be used. In general, the solutions finally obtained require previous purification from an appreciable quantity of alien substances. These substances are initially insignificant impurities, but eventually they too are concentrated; they pass into solution from the reagents or as a result of the partial dissolution of the material of the vessel. It is understandable that, under these conditions, the purity of the initial reagents and the stability of the material of the vessel walls against the action of the reagents used acquire special importance. It must, however, be emphasized that purity of the reagents is especially important in ultramicroanalysis only in the case of concentration. For work on the microscope stage the normal chemical reagents are adequate, because the quantity used is reduced proportionally to the quantity of the substance under study.

The increase in the relative surface area that occurs in ultramicroanalysis, in some cases affects the speed of crystallization from solutions and the form of the crystals evolved.

In the transition to the ultramicroscale there is also an increase in the relative free surface of liquids because of the large curvature of the meniscus in capillaries. Therefore the speed of evaporation of solutions, which is directly proportional to the free surface of the liquid, here becomes quite considerable. The speed of evaporation at atmospheric pressure, as is well known, is expressed by the approximate formula:

$$v = kS(P - p) \tag{2}$$

where S is the free surface of the liquid; P the pressure of the saturated vapours at the given temperature; p the pressure of the vapours above the liquid; k a constant. According to kinetic theory, the change in vapour pressure Δp with curvature of the liquid surface is expressed by the equation:

$$\frac{\Delta p}{P} = \frac{2\sigma M}{rd \times RT} \tag{3}$$

where σ is the surface tension; d the density of the liquid; r the radius of curvature; M the molecular weight; R the universal gas constant; T the absolute temperature. Liquids which wet a capillary, owing to the large curvature of the concave surface, have a considerably lower vapour pressure than in wide vessels. Nonetheless, evaporation proceeds incomparably faster, because the free surface of the liquid is increased relatively much more than the vapour pressure is reduced. Thus, for example, the free surface of a liquid placed in a capillary of 0·6 mm dia. is not 0·3 mm², like a plane surface of the same dia., but about 0·6 mm², while the vapour pressure above a meniscus of corresponding curvature is reduced altogether by 5 per cent. Furthermore, a solution in a capillary is in much more favourable conditions for heat transfer.

The procedure used in ultramicroanalysis to reduce the rate of evaporation of liquids from capillaries is to work in a moist atmosphere. Aqueous salt solutions, which have a lower vapour pressure than water, evaporate, all other things being equal, more slowly than the latter, but not to such a degree as to preclude the possibility of working in a moist atmosphere. In work in a moist atmosphere the volume of saturated salt solutions in capillaries is appreciably increased. This results from the equalization of the vapour pressure of the vapours over the saturated solution in the capillary in a system of vapours over pure water (moist atmosphere). The hygroscopicity of the solute is also an important consideration. In a moist atmosphere one should not, therefore, work with saturated salt solutions and concentrated acids.

Table 3 below confirms the above discussion.

TABLE 3. THE CHANGE IN VOLUME OF LIQUID IN CAPILLARIES IN RELATION TO THE MOISTURE OF THE ATMOSPHERE

Substance	Diameter of capillary, mm	Volume of solution, mm³	Change in volume (%) in 1 min relative to the initial volume	
			In normal atmosphere	In moist atmosphere
Water	0·12	0·02	−1·0	−0·1
1 M solution of potassium nitrate	0·12	0·02	−0·4	−0·06
Saturated solution of calcium chloride	0·12	0·02	+0.02	+0·6

Organic liquids, which are used in the preparation of solutions or in extractions, evaporate especially quickly, which is explained either by the small latent heats of evaporation of these substances or by their high vapour pressures. Such substances, like ether and chloroform, which have particularly high vapour pressures, are expelled from thin capillaries which are sealed at one end by the action of their own vapours, so that they form at the open end of the capillary a rapidly evaporating drop. The rate of evaporation of an organic fluid may be reduced by working in an atmosphere of the vapour of the relevant substance.

Besides the increased adsorption of the substance from the solution on to the walls of the vessel and the higher rate of evaporation of the liquid, the increase in the relative surface area of the liquid has the additional consequence that there is an increase in the surface tension forces, which attain an appreciable magnitude in work in capillaries. This fact must be kept in view especially in the development of the experimental technique of ultramicroanalysis. On the one hand, the position is complicated by the need to overcome the surface tension forces in transferring a liquid from one capillary to another. On the other, it prevents the possibility of loss of solution by spilling and also, thanks to the stable position of the meniscus (within the limits of the rate of evaporation), allows the accurate measuring of solutions. In work with capillaries an important part is played by the cleanliness of the surface of the liquid. The presence in the solution of surface-active agents spoils the wetting by the solution of the surface of the glass, which leads to error in determinations. As is well known, salt solutions have a greater surface tension than water, the tension growing approximately proportionately to the number of equivalents of the dissolved salt. This increase in the surface tension explains the creep of salts (for example, of ammonium nitrate), which is a serious difficulty in work with capillaries. Work is also impeded by the creep of precipitates over the vessel walls (for example, of the precipitate of nickel dimethylglyoxime).

Thanks to the increase in the surface tension forces, gas evolving from solutions in capillaries behaves quite differently: a gas bubble often fails to reach the surface of the liquid and remains below. The later gas bubbles join it and in time form a large bubble which breaks the solution into two isolated parts. This surface tension effect is also helped by the horizontal position of the capillaries. In ultramicroanalysis the heating of a liquid to boiling point, which is characterized by the appearance of steam bubbles below the surface of the liquid and their subsequent evolution, is entirely out of the question.

Alimarin and Petrikova [54] overcome these phenomena connected with the size of the surface of contact of solutions with the vessel walls, and also those connected with the use of capillaries as vessels, by covering the walls of their microapparatus with a film of an organic silicon compound.

The authors made the glass walls of their vessels unwettable by treating their carefully cleaned surfaces with a 3 per cent solution of methyltrichlorsilane (CH_3SiCl_3) in carbon tetrachloride, after which they heated the vessels for an hour at 120–130°. The coating thus obtained is stable against the action of aqueous salt solutions and dilute acids, but less stable in alkaline solutions. The relevant data are given in Table 4.

TABLE 4. STABILITY OF THE NON-WETTING FILM
(AT ROOM TEMPERATURE)

Concentration of solutions, N	Time, hr			
	HCl	HNO$_3$	H$_2$SO$_4$	NaOH
0·1	>15	>15	>15	2
0·5	>15	2·5	>15	1
1·0	3	1·5	1·5	0·5
3·0	1	1	1	0·25
6·0	0·5	0·5	0·5	—

The glass surface of vessels, when coated with this methyltrichlorsilane film, is not wetted by aqueous solutions, which makes it possible to use them without rinsing between operations. By using cobalt nitrate labelled with ^{60}Co and measuring the γ-radiation of the washing water and the vessels, one can satisfy oneself that, even with the most careful emptying of microapparatus, there remains on the walls 0·5–2 per cent of the solution. When glassware with treated walls is used, this phenomenon is not observed. The titration error connected with the speed with which a solution flows out of a horizontal burette is also reduced to zero [11].

The poor wetting of a treated surface by aqueous solutions is a result of the reduction in the surface tension at the boundary between this surface and the solution. This phenomenon, therefore, like the creep of salts on to the external walls of capillary vessels (Fig. 1)

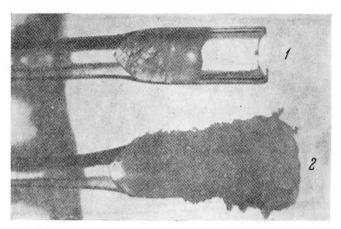

FIG. 1. Effect of treating microvessel walls with anti-wetting agent:
1—vessel treated with methyltrichlorsilane; 2—untreated.

and also of calomel electrodes, is eliminated by treatment with an anti-wetting agent.

The reduction in the surface tension caused by this treatment has no undesirable effect on the retention of the solution in a horizontal capillary vessel—loss of solution from such apparatus as a result of spillage occurs only if the vessel is shaken vigorously. On the other hand, an aqueous solution will no longer rise by itself from a wider vessel into such a treated capillary. In this connexion it should be noted that, if a treated burette is operated by a gravity arrangement, a much greater difference in levels than usual is needed to draw solution into the burette.

We may also note at this point that a methyltrichlorsilane film is a successful substitute for paraffin on the condenser rod [33].

We have considered above in detail the effect of the curvature of the liquid surface in capillaries on the rate of evaporation of liquids from them.

The free surface of a liquid in a treated capillary vessel is considerably reduced by the levelling off of the meniscus (the angle of contact on a treated surface is 90–110°, while it is practically

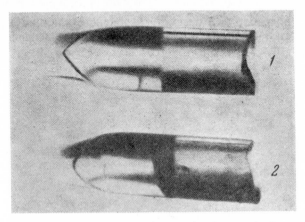

FIG. 2. Position of the meniscus in microvessels: 1—treated; 2—untreated.

zero on a normal glass surface, as may be seen from Fig. 2). In consequence the rate of evaporation from such vessels is significantly reduced.

Further, a flat meniscus permits easier and more precise measurements of volume in burettes and glassware when a micrometer eyepiece is used, because only one, always strictly determinate line of the meniscus is seen. El-Badry and Wilson [39] also recommend putting a film of "Teddol" on the inner surface of measuring capillaries for this reason. The high ratio S/v which obtains in ultramicroanalysis makes it necessary to pay particular attention to the possibility of losing material by adsorption on the vessel walls, even from solutions of normal concentrations. Interaction between the solution and the glass may be prevented by treating the walls of the vessel with an anti-wetting film. Experiments have been carried out which show that adsorption losses are significantly reduced when such vessels are used. The use of labelled atoms for the study of adsorption has made it possible to obtain reliable results directly and quickly.

Experiments have been performed with RaE and ^{110}Ag for solutions of varying acidity. The results of these experiments are given in Table 5.

TABLE 5. THE ADSORPTION OF RaE AND ^{110}Ag ON THE WALLS OF MICROVESSELS ($S/v = 15$)

Isotope	Concentration of element, g/ml	Concentration of HNO_3, N	Soaking time, hr	Total activity of solution and rinse waters, imps/min		Activity of vessel walls, imps/min		Adsorption (%)	
				I	II	I	II	I	II
RaE	10^{-14}	0·1	1	7050	7300	980	160	14	2·2
		0·1	1	4200	3070	670	108	17	3·5
		0·1	22	—	2900	—	130	—	4·5
		0·1	20	5300	6000	795	455	15	7·6
		0·5	0·66	7950	8600	48	23	0·6	0·27
		0·5	2	975	1100	33	18	3·4	1·65
		0·3	3·5	675	690	27	13	4·0	1·85
^{110}Ag	80	0·C01	0·66	1063	915	81	32	7·6	3·5

Note: I—normal microvessel; II—microvessel with walls treated with anti-wetting agent.

The table shows that two, three and even seven times less material is adsorbed on to treated walls, the difference being the greater the less acid the solution. Thus the greatest effect can be obtained from the use of treated vessels when neutral aqueous solutions are used: this is a substantial gain, because adsorption from strongly acidic solutions is in general small.

Thus, the use of a methyltrichlorsilane coating in ultramicro-analysis has the following advantages:

(1) the need to rinse vessels is eliminated;

(2) the normal titration error, arising from the speed with which solutions flow out of a horizontal burette, is reduced to zero;

(3) the creep of salts on to the external walls of the vessels is prevented;

(4) the rate of evaporation out of small volumes is significantly reduced by the levelling off of the meniscus;

(5) the precision with which solutions can be measured in capillaries is increased; and

(6) adsorption losses on the walls of vessels are substantially reduced.

We must, therefore, recommend that in ultramicroanalysis glassware should be treated with an anti-wetting agent before use.

CHAPTER II

GENERAL APPARATUS

As HAS been pointed out above, work with small volumes of solutions requires special apparatus and experimental techniques. The vessels used are microvessels of special form, being 0·5–1·5 mm in diameter and made from capillaries. The transfer of liquids is effected by a micropipette. This is a capillary with its tip drawn out to a diameter of 0·02–0·04 mm. The pipette is fitted with a piston device. To protect the small volumes from rapid evaporation work is carried out in the so-called moist chamber. Sufficiently reliable handling of the volumes of solutions and precipitates investigated in ultramicroanalysis is achieved by mechanical devices (movable microscope stage and manipulators), with simultaneous observation through a microscope, which creates an impression of work on the normal scale. The microscope and manipulators are fixed on the same base-plate. The moist chamber with the vessels is placed on the stage, while the necessary implements are fixed in the manipulators. This assembly (Fig. 3) is used for ultramicrochemical investigations. Only a few operations are carried out without the microscope.

It should be noted that the greater part of the ancillary apparatus must be made by the experimenter himself, because even an expert technician at times experiences great difficulty through inadequate appreciation of the specific requirements of the work.

THE MICROSCOPE

An ordinary microscope with a movable stage, allowing displacement and rotation of the object, is very convenient for ultramicroanalytical research. For example, El-Badry and Wilson [39] use a petrographic microscope, while Alimarin and Petrikova [48] use a binocular biological microscope.

11

The overall magnification of the microscope, the product of the magnification of the objective and eyepiece, must be in the region of 25–100. It is convenient to use objectives $\times 3$–4, $\times 8$, and eyepieces magnifying 7, 10 and 15 times.

The microscope eyepiece is equipped with an eyepiece micrometer,

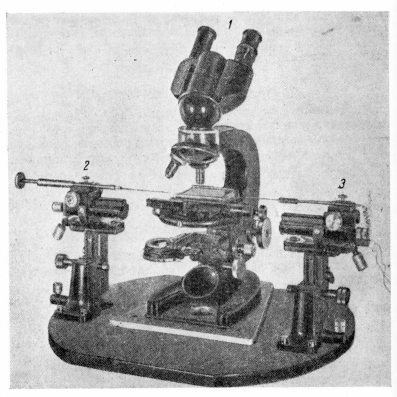

FIG. 3. The fundamental instrument for chemical ultramicroanalysis: 1—the microscope; 2 and 3—the micromanipulators.

which must be calibrated for each given pair of objective and eyepiece against a known scale.

When incident light is used as the source of illumination, observations are most conveniently made by daylight. El-Badry and Wilson [39] are also of this opinion, though Benedetti-Pichler [33] recommends the use of artificial illumination. For observation in reflected light, for example, in work on the condenser rod, a microlamp must be used [33].

MICROMANIPULATORS

Micromanipulators are the mechanical device used to move the greater part of the apparatus employed in ultramicroanalysis.

The number and disposition of the manipulators needed is determined by the number of instruments, that are required simultaneously for carrying out an operation, and the convenience of moving them; in any event, there will be not less than two.

The construction of the manipulators may vary, but there should be three smooth progressive displacements (back and forth, up and down, left and right) and rotation about an axis; it should also be possible to fix the instruments firmly in the clamping device.

Brindle and Wilson [56] consider that micromanipulators for chemical purposes must satisfy the following requirements:

(1) they must have a vertical movement of about 4 cm; this is needed so that the instrument held by the manipulator may be set at the desired height relative to the microscope stage;

(2) they must be able to move in the horizontal plane towards and away from the object. This movement must also be of about 4 cm to ensure that the working part of any instrument can be brought up under the microscope objective and positioned in the field of view;

(3) they must have a sufficient lateral movement (left and right) so that the necessary manipulations outside the field of view can be made;

(4) they must have fine control, especially for the lateral movement, so that the instruments can be co-ordinated relative to the vessel placed on the microscope stage;

(5) an inclination of $\pm 20°$ to the central axis must be available; and

(6) they must damp vibrations.

Alvarez-Querol [57] proposes a somewhat different construction: this type of manipulator is easily made from the parts of an old microscope (Fig. 4, 1). In general, many types of construction for various purposes have been described in the literature [58–67]; all may be used by the chemist in one way or another. In Fig. 4, 2 we give a diagram showing the principle of Fonbrune's interesting manipulator.*

The manipulators are placed on a metal [39, 48] or wooden [33] base-plate, in the middle of which stands the microscope (see Fig. 3). The microscope need not be fixed to the plate (contary to Benedetti-

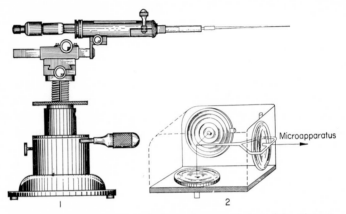

Fig. 4. Various types of manipulator: 1—general view of the Alvarez-Querol manipulator; 2—general scheme of the Fonbrune manipulator.

Pichler's recommendation) because it is sufficiently massive, and in the course of the work there is no need for abrupt movements such as might lead to a displacement of the microscope. A free-standing microscope has the advantage that, in case of need, it can be moved in any desired direction.

PISTON ATTACHMENT FOR THE MICROPIPETTE

To fix the pipette in the clamping device of the manipulator a holder is needed, and some piston arrangement is needed for effecting transfer of liquids by means of the pipette. The so-called piston attachment described below fulfils both these functions.

* P. FONBRUNE, *Technique de Micromanipulation*, Paris (1949).

The construction of the attachment, which is made of brass or stainless steel, is shown in Fig. 5, 1. The piston attachment consists of two cylindrical parts a and b, joined by a screw thread. Into the opening of part b there fits a screw of 0·15 mm pitch, ending in a piston, which is a metal beam of 2 mm dia. When parts a and b are joined, the piston fits tightly into the through hole in part a, which widens out towards the opposite end. A thin rubber washer

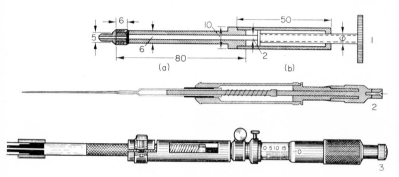

FIG. 5. Various types of piston attachments for micropipettes.

is placed on the metal wall formed by the different diameter of the openings; this is followed by a metal bush and clamped by a screw cap. The rubber washer, bushing and cap are used to fix the pipette.

Part a of the piston attachment is filled with water, which moves up it a certain distance thanks to the capillary forces, when the pipette is set in. The piston is then used to create positive or negative pressure, so that the solution to be transferred is either sucked into, or forced out of, the end of the pipette.

The piston attachment described by Benedetti-Pichler [33] is not convenient to use. It is unwieldy and difficult to prepare for work: the complicated system proposed makes it almost impossible to fill without air bubbles, and this in turn makes it unsuitable. Alvarez-Querol [57] uses as a piston attachment a 1-ml syringe, the piston of which is moved by a micrometer screw set in the brass body of the instrument with the syringe (Fig. 5.2).

El-Badry and Wilson [39] describe a piston attachment of similar construction; they recommend that the pipette be joined to the piston attachment by a rubber sleeve (Fig. 5, 3).

THE MOIST CHAMBER AND APPARATUS HOLDER

The chamber is a glass-covered brass [33] or Plexiglass [39] frame (Fig. 6). In all the models described there is in the side-walls a

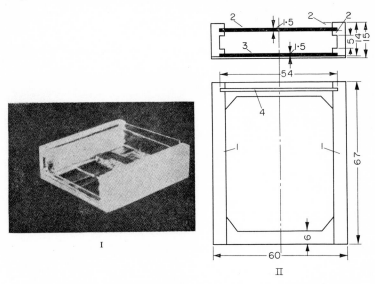

FIG. 6. Chamber for holding microvessels: I—general view; II—front and top view: 1 and 4—Plexiglass frames and wall; 2 and 3—glass lid and bottom.

longitudinal channel at the top for the glass cover and a transverse one for the rear wall. A number of workers [33, 48] use chambers where the bottom is fitted into slots in the lower part of the side-walls, but El-Badry and Wilson [39] use one where the bottom is screwed to the side-walls.

The moist atmosphere in the chamber is provided by cotton-wool soaked in water [33, 48] or strips of filter paper [39] placed in a wide longitudinal channel in the side-walls, or directly on the bottom of the chamber.

The apparatus is placed in a special holder in the chamber (see Fig. 16). Several types of such holders have been suggested.

Benedetti-Pichler [33] recommends the use of a glass plate, 24 × 35 × 7 mm in size, covered by a layer of Vaseline about 1 mm thick, in which the apparatus is fixed (Fig. 7, 1). This type of

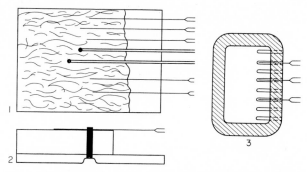

FIG. 7. Microvessel holder: 1 and 3—top view; 2—side view.

holder is not entirely convenient, because the stem of the vessel must be freed from the Vaseline layer each time it is removed.

It is better practice to use a plastic plate with a rubber band [39] to hold the apparatus (Fig. 7, 2) or a similar plate 40 × 25 × 4 mm in size with holes and a thin rubber band round the edge (Fig. 7, 3) [46].

MICROAPPARATUS

The glassware used in ultramicroanalysis is a special kind of capillary microapparatus, first described by Benedetti-Pichler [33]. It is made from capillaries of 0·5–1·5 mm dia. drawn out in the flame of a gas-jet from glass tubes or (if necessary) from tubes of transparent fused quartz.

Cut the tubes into 10–15 cm lengths, wash with soapy water and then chromic acid inside and out. Rinse with ordinary, then with distilled, water and alcohol, and then dry. From the dry tubes draw out capillaries, cut them in pieces 20–30 cm long, seal both ends and store in tall cylinders with lids that fit over the outside.

3

Next make the apparatus from the capillaries so obtained in a microflame. Always use tweezers to pick up and move microapparatus. Ophthalmic tweezers are the most convenient to use, because they give a good grip on the capillaries thanks to the special "lock" at their tip.

A *microflame* can be obtained by means of a microburner, which is not difficult to make.

Bend a glass (or better, quartz) tube at right angles and draw the end out into a capillary of the desired diameter. Attach a rubber tube to the thick end of the glass tube and attach to a gas tap.

The flow of gas is controlled by a glass tap situated between the burner and the gas tap. Bendetti-Pichler also describes a similar microburner with this difference, that the gas flow is regulated by a screw clamp, while the burner itself stands on glass feet [33].

The Micropipette

The micropipette is a capillary 10–12 cm long and 0·5–1 mm in diameter, with its tip drawn out some 5–7 mm, the diameter being 20–40 μ (Fig. 8, 1).

The tip of the capillary is drawn out in a microflame 2–3 mm high. Place the capillary horizontally in the upper part of the flame and remove it quickly when it softens; then draw it out till it parts.

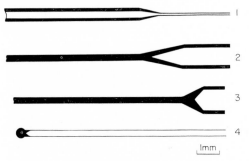

FIG. 8. Microapparatus: 1—micropipette; 2—microvessel; 3—capillary cone; 4—measuring capillary.

The microflame must be arranged at a convenient working height; the sides of the palms should rest on the table. The finished pipettes are sealed at the broad end and stored in the same way as the capillaries.

Microvessels

The reactants are placed in capillary microvessels. A microvessel is a short, cone-shaped capillary 3–5 mm long and 0·5–1 mm in diameter. The end of the cone-shaped part is drawn out into a thin stem 0·3 mm in diameter and 1·5–2·0 cm in length (Fig. 8, 2).

To make a microvessel, take a suitable capillary and hold it in a microflame. After a time, when the hollow capillary turns into a solid, molten, fused mass, remove it from the flame and, without letting it cool, draw out the stem. Cut the stem in half and leave a sufficient length of capillary, so making two microvessels.

The most convenient capillaries for making vessels have a wall thickness of 0·06–0·07 mm.

For cutting the capillaries use a knife made of a hard alloy with a fine cutting edge.

To calibrate the vessels, measure their diameter. Store them in a box with a lid or in a screw-top container which, in turn, is kept under a bell-jar. Label the box with the calibration data.

Capillary Cones

A capillary cone is essentially a microvessel with a shorter capillary part about 2 mm long, half of which consists of a conical part with a fairly large cone angle (Fig. 8, 3). The large angle of the conical part is necessary, because, without it, filling the cone with solution and collecting a precipitate on the bottom is complicated.

Capillary cones are made and stored in the same way as microvessels. The form of the bottom of each cone made should be checked under a microscope.

Measuring Capillaries

For measuring out volumes of the order of 10^{-8}–10^{-9} ml, measuring capillaries, 2–3 cm in length and 0·5–0·2 mm in diameter, are used (Fig. 8, 4).

To make such a capillary, take a thick-walled capillary about 1 mm in diameter and draw it out in a microflame to the required diameter; then cut it into pieces some 2–3 cm long. Measure the diameter of the capillaries obtained at both ends.

Uniformity of diameter along the whole length is an important requirement in a measuring capillary. The cross-section must be circular.

El-Badry and Wilson [39] recommend that each individual measuring capillary should be kept in a separate, labelled capillary sealed at both ends.

The Condenser Rod

A number of qualitative reactions under the microscope can be produced on the illuminated surface of a condenser rod [33]. These are microcrystalline reactions on the ultramicroscale.*

The illuminated surface is a shear plane in the thin part of the condenser rod, which is about 0·3 mm in diameter (Fig. 9).

If a light beam I is directed on to the rod through F, then the light

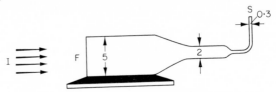

FIG. 9. Condenser rod (profile).

will be condensed on the surface S; this provides sufficiently powerful illumination for the observation of reactions.

The condenser rod is made from an ordinary rod of clear, low melting point glass 4–5 mm in diameter.

Draw the rod down to 2 mm diameter so that there is a sharp transition. Then draw it down to a fibre of 0·3 mm dia. Score the fibre and break it off at a distance of 2 cm from the second transition. Cut the thick part of the rod in such a way that it is 10–12 mm long with a smooth surface at the cutting point. Place the fibre horizontally in a microflame: it will bend under its own weight. Then, holding the rod by the thick part, immerse the fibre almost up to the bend in molten paraffin (and slowly lift out) or into a silicon polymer solution (with subsequent heating to 120–130°; see p. 6). Next score the fibre 5 mm from the bend and break it off

* Korenman's book [68] is a valuable handbook for microcrystalline reactions.

with tweezers. The plane of the surface resulting must be perpendicular to the axis of the fibre.

The film of paraffin or silicon polymer on the fibre prevents the solution placed on the surface from running off.

The condenser rod is fixed to a cover slip with paraffin.

Glass Rod for Reactions on Fibres

In microchemistry it is a common technique to produce qualitative reactions on cotton and silk fibres [33].

To produce these reactions under the microscope El-Badry and Wilson [39] suggest that the fibre should be affixed to a piece of glass rod 0·5 cm in diameter and 2·5–3 cm long, or to a glass fibre bent double (Fig. 10), this in its turn being fixed in the vessel holder in the chamber. The fibre is fixed to the glass rod with starch paste.

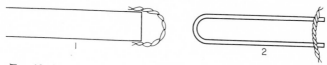

FIG. 10. Holder for reactions on fibres: 1—glass rod; 2—filament.

Place the fibre in a horizontal position and soak it with the reagent from the tip of a rod or capillary. Then introduce it into the field of view of the microscope, bring up the pipette tip, force out a drop and move it towards the fibre until the latter breaks the surface of the drop. Then, after a time, force the whole of the solution gradually out of the pipette on to the fibre.

SOME ANCILLARY APPARATUS

The Centrifuge

The separation of small precipitates from solution, and also the collection of liquid from the walls of vessels into the cone-shaped part, is effected by centrifugation. Both a motor-driven and a hand-turned centrifuge can be used with equal success. Figure 11 shows a hand centrifuge with a 100 to 1 gear ratio; thus, rotation of the handle at 50–80 rev/min means that the disk with the microtest-tubes rotates at 5000–8000 rev/min.

A capillary cone is not placed directly into the microtest-tube, but

FIG. 11. Microcentrifuge and arrangement of the vessel in the centrifuge tube: 1—centrifuge; 2—lid.

first into a capillary (Fig. 11); this reduces the air space around the cone and thus reduces the rate of evaporation of the solution.

Device for Use with Gaseous Reagents

The use of gaseous reagents in ultramicroanalysis permits the simplification of the analytical technique. This is a very elegant method. By replacing the addition of reagent by pipette, it excludes the complications associated with that procedure, i.e., the possibility of the solution diffusing into the pipette with the reagent, and the adhesion of the precipitate formed to the pipette tip during mixing. When several reactions are to be done in succession, the use of gaseous reagents makes it possible to dissolve a precipitate in the course of the analysis without separating the solution from the precipitate, or evaporating the solution before addition of the reagent. On the other hand, some reactions are normally done with gaseous reagents, for example, the precipitation of sulphides.

Small volumes of solutions are saturated with gas, not by forcing the gas into them, but by absorption of gas by them from a gas-saturated atmosphere. This method is used when exact measurement of the precipitating agent or solvent is not required.

A convenient device for treating solutions in cones with gaseous reagents is that shown in Fig. 12. This consists of a vessel (1) with

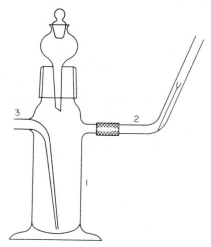

FIG. 12. Apparatus for use with gaseous reagents.

a side tube and a capillary (2), which is bent at an obtuse angle. The gaseous reagent fills the vessel.

First take the microcone containing the solution from the moist chamber and place it in a capillary 1·5–2 mm in diameter and with a stem 7–8 cm long that has been bent in a microflame. Then cover the capillary with a piece of cotton wool. On the bottom of the vessel, if this is necessary to obtain the gas, pour a solid substance (for example, sodium sulphide). Connect the capillary to the vessel with a rubber sleeve, then pour the other reactant (for example, sulphuric acid) into the vessel through a funnel, whereupon it reacts with the solid reactant to form a gas.

The gas evolved fills the vessel and the capillary, and is absorbed by the solution in the cone. It is advisable to put a small piece of cotton wool not too firmly into the side tube to prevent spray from the solution finding its way from the vessel into the capillary.

If the gaseous reagent can be obtained from a liquid (for example, filling the vessel with concentrated ammonia solution is enough to saturate the solution in the cone with ammonia), then the vessel is filled with the solution after the capillary has been connected and air is blown through the tube (3).

The formation of precipitates (especially those that are brightly coloured) and the solution may be observed either with the naked eye or with a lens.

Microheaters

Electrical microheaters or a heating block are used to heat and evaporate solutions in capillary cones. We describe two types of electrical microheater.

(a) The part which has the direct heating effect is a V-shaped wire made of a copper–nickel alloy; it is 5 cm long and 0·5 mm in

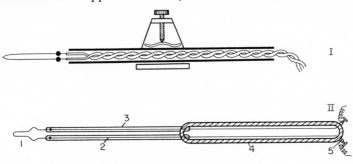

FIG. 13. Microheaters.

diameter (Fig. 13, I). At the point of bending the wire is filed down to a diameter of 0·1–0·2 mm. The ends of this wire are connected to ordinary insulated copper wire, which is passed through a glass tube and fixed at the exit with insulating tape.

(b) The actual heating element is the tip of a platinum wire about 0·2 mm in diameter. The wire (1), about 3 cm long, is bent as in Fig. 13, II, and pressed into copper leads: the point of contact is soldered with silver. The copper leads (2) are insulated by the capillaries (3) and passed through an ebony holder (4) and terminals (5).

The power for these heaters is provided by a voltage-reducing transformer, the voltage being reduced to about 6 V. The amount of heating in either case is rheostatically controlled. The auto-transformers LATR-1 and LATR-2 are convenient for this purpose.

The heating block is an aluminium cylinder with holes drilled into it for a thermometer and the capillaries. It is heated by a microburner with a pencil flame. The temperature required is obtained by regulating the flame. The capillary cones are placed in the openings in the block in protective capillaries.

Supplementary Glass-ware

The reagents required are kept in test-tubes with pipettes. The test-tubes in turn are placed in convenient stands. The reagent is drawn into the micropipette from a special cone of 4–5 mm dia., which is made similarly to a capillary cone: the stem is 1·5–2 mm in diameter, 6–7 cm long and bent at right angles.

If this cone is filled with water, the pipette can be washed out. This is more convenient than the method proposed by Benedetti-Pichler—to wash with a drop hanging from the tip of a glass-tube.

SETTING UP THE APPARATUS

The plate on which the microscope and manipulators are mounted (see p. 12) should be placed on a sufficiently stable laboratory table. The experimentalist should sit at the microscope comfortably and without strain, so that he can easily do the manipulations required. The right hand is used to control the manipulator, the left the movable stage with the chamber.

Calibration of the Micrometer Eye-piece

The value of a division on the micrometer varies according to the magnification of the objective and eyepiece used. It must, therefore, be calibrated for each given magnification. This is done by means of a standard micrometer with 0·01 mm divisions.

Place the standard micrometer on the microscope stage so that the zero division of the scale coincides with the zero division of the micrometer eyepiece, and then determine the number of divisions of the standard

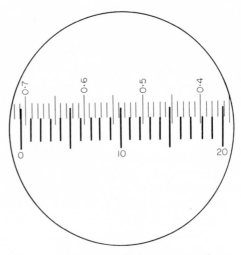

FIG. 14. Calibration of micrometer eyepiece.

to which a given number of divisions of the micrometer eyepiece corresponds (Fig. 14). Then calculate the value of one division of the micrometer eyepiece for the given magnification and make a note of it.

Calibration of the Microvessels

A microvessel is calibrated by measuring its diameter. Place the object to be calibrated vertically on the microscope stage and measure its diameter in divisions of the eyepiece micrometer. The vessel (cone, measuring capillary) is set up with its stem in a section of thick-walled capillary with internal diameter close to that of the stem. Convert the results into millimetres and calculate the mean diameter. The deviation from the mean should not exceed 5 per cent.

From the mean diameter calculate the length of the vessel (measuring capillary) corresponding to a volume of 1 λ by the formula:

$$L_{1\lambda} = \frac{4}{\pi D^2 \Delta} \text{ (div)} \tag{4}$$

where D is the diameter of the capillary in millimetres; Δ the value of a division of the eyepiece micrometer for the given magnification in millimetres.

It is convenient to reduce the data obtained to tabular form.

Preparing the Piston Attachment

A micropipette is used with a piston attachment to control the flow of liquid. The preparation of this piston attachment is an important operation, because success in analysis depends essentially on the normal functioning of the pipette.

The device described above (see Fig. 5, 1) is prepared as follows.

Turn the screw (1) till the piston is entirely clear of part b. Then smear the piston thickly with vacuum grease and screw it back in again till about 1 cm of the piston remains outside part b.

Fit a piece of rubber tubing (1) (see Fig. 15) on the narrow end of the piston attachment and so fill part a with distilled water by means of the syringe (2): the meniscus should come about half way up the glass connecting tube (3). Lift part a clear of the water and pinch the rubber tube (1) in the fingers at the point where it is joined to the glass tube and carefully remove the rubber tubing together with part a. Keeping the rubber tubing pinched in the fingers, insert the piston into the opening of part a, remove the rubber tubing and screw the two halves of the piston attachment together.

Place a rubber washer on the metal diaphragm in part a and use filter paper to remove any excess water on the washer. Place a sleeve and cap on the pipette and insert it into the device. Screw the cap up tight. Turn the piston screw either way until the meniscus of the hydraulic fluid in the pipette is about 1–2 cm from the cap.

If the device has been assembled correctly, i.e., if there are no air bubbles, every turn of the piston screw will produce a smooth movement of the meniscus of the hydraulic fluid. If, however, there are air bubbles, turning the screw fails for a time to produce any movement of the water: then it will suddenly move forward sharply. This situation makes it quite impossible to work with the pipette, and the preparation of the device must be repeated.

For such a repetition clean the inner surface of part a carefully of every trace of the grease; for example, rinse it in benzene. Then wash with a concentrated solution of caustic alkali, rinse with water, and only then start the preparation anew. Otherwise, the non-wettability of the inner surface of part *a* will prevent successful assembly of the device. If, however, the pipette should for any

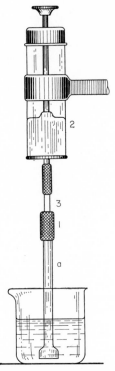

Fig. 15. First stage in loading the piston attachment.

reason stop working properly while the piston attachment is still in good order, the following action should be taken.

Unscrew the cap and remove the unserviceable pipette. Also remove the bushing and the rubber washer and turn the screw (1) till a drop of the hydraulic fluid appears in the opening. Then replace the rubber washer and insert a fresh pipette, as described above.

Furnishing the Moist Chamber

The vessels with the reagents, the capillary cones in which the reactions are done and the measuring capillaries needed for an experiment are placed in the moist chamber (Fig. 16).

Use tweezers to place the number of vessels and cones required in the holder. It is convenient to work with the ends of the capillary parts of

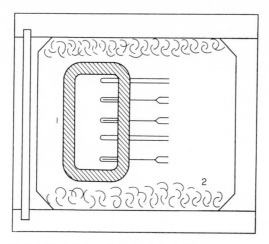

FIG. 16. Moist chamber with vessels (top view): 1—microvessel holder; 2—moist cotton wool.

the vessels and cones, and the ends of the measuring capillaries in one straight line.

Remove the lid of the chamber from its grooves and put moist cotton wool or paper in the middle wide channels on either side. On the bottom of the chamber place the holder with the vessels and fix it in place with plasticine. Before closing the chamber, it is advisable to treat the inner surface of the lid with a film of some substance to protect the glass from condensation (a respirator pencil is available for this). Otherwise, condensate will collect on the lid during the operation, making observation difficult.

ON TECHNIQUES OF WORKING WITH SMALL VOLUMES

The techniques used for the various chemical operations with small volumes of solutions are specific in character and not as yet sufficiently standardized. However, the simplest methods involving the microscope and manipulators are described in detail by Benedetti-Pichler [33]: filling vessels with solutions by means of micropipettes, extracting a definite volume of solution from a vessel, reactions in capillary cones, separation of precipitate from solution, dissolution of precipitates, heating of solutions, addition of solid reagents to a solution, etc.

We, therefore, give below a more or less full description of the apparatus used, with details of the experimental procedures only in some cases—those that are described for the first time.

Let us note that, normally, the vessels required are placed in the moist chamber on the microscope stage, the remaining instruments being fixed in the manipulators. When the stage and manipulators are moved towards one another, the object and the instruments needed for its investigation are brought into the field of view of the microscope, where the various operations are observed.

CHAPTER III

QUALITATIVE ANALYSIS

THE presence of some element in an analytical sample is detected, as is well known, by the characteristic colour of its various compounds, by its property of forming precipitates under certain conditions, by the type of crystals formed, and so on. Very useful general information on methods of qualitative analysis is to be found in the books of Alekseyev,* Klyachko and Shapiro,† and Okáč,‡ and on methods of qualitative microanalysis in a monograph by Malissa and Benedetti-Pichler.§ In qualitative analysis on the microscope stage special apparatus and techniques are used, which are described below.

OBSERVATION OF THE COLOUR OF SOLUTIONS

Under certain conditions a desired component of a solution will form a coloured complex with a certain reagent, and its presence in the solution can thus be detected.

This method is more sensitive and therefore permits the detection of smaller quantities of a substance than, for example, the method of precipitation. The sensitivity of the reaction is characterized by two mutually related quantities: the minimum detectable amount and the minimum concentration.

* V. N. ALEKSEYEV, *A Course of Qualitative Chemical Semimicro-Analysis* (Kurs kachestvennogo khimicheskogo polumikroanaliza), Goskhimizdat, Moscow (1958).

† YU. A. KLYACHKO and S. A. SHAPIRO, *A Course of Chemical Qualitative Analysis* (Kurs khimicheskogo kachestvennogo analiza), Goskhimizdat, Moscow (1960).

‡ A. OKÁČ, *Analytická Chemie kvalitativni*, Praha (1956).

§ H. MALISSA and A. BENEDETTI-PICHLER, *Monographien aus dem Gebiete der qualitativen Mikroanlyse*, vol. 1. *Anorganische qualitative Mikroanalyse*, Vienna (1958).

The minimum detectable amount is the least quantity of a substance that can be detected by a given reagent under certain determined conditions of observation of the reaction products.

The minimum concentration shows in how dilute a solution the reaction will still give a positive result under the given conditions of observation.

The minimum concentration is normally expressed as the ratio of unit weight of the substance to be detected in the solution, to the weight or volume of the solvent. From the volume in which the reaction occurs it is possible to calculate the minimum concentration from the minimum detectable amount and vice versa:

$$c_{\min} = 1 : \frac{v}{m} \tag{5}$$

$$m = c_{\min} \times v, \tag{6}$$

where $c_{\min}$ is the minimum concentration, m the minimum detectable amount in grammes, v the volume of solution, in millilitres.

The problem of the minimum quantity of a substance needed for a reaction is solved on the basis of the known sensitivity of the reaction.*

If N is Avogadro's number, M the molecular weight, 10^{-x} the minimum detectable amount, then the substance in the solution can be detected if there are a molecules present, where a is given by

$$a = \frac{N}{M} \times 10^{-x}. \tag{7}$$

At present, the mean sensitivity of colour reactions is 10^{-8} g in 1 ml.

Relating this sensitivity to the volumes met in ultramicroanalysis (10^{-3}–10^{-4} ml), we obtain a figure of 10^{-12} g. Taking $M = 100$ and using the data adduced, we find the number of molecules needed for the detection of a substance:

$$a = \frac{6 \times 10^{23}}{100} \times 10^{-12} = 6 \times 10^9 \text{ molecules.}$$

* L. M. KUL'BERG, G. S. AL'TERZON and R. P. VEL'TMAN, *Drop Analysis* (*Kapel'nyi analiz*), Goskhimizdat, Moscow (1951).

Thus, if the presence of a substance in the form of a coloured complex is to be detected, there must be at least six thousand million molecules present. Within the limits of the quantity of some substance detectable by this method it is, of course, possible to vary the conditions so as to increase the sensitivity of a given determination.

The intensity of the colour of a solution depends on the presence of the appropriate quantity of the coloured substance in the path of the light beam. The nature of a coloured substance is characterized by the magnitude of its coefficient of extinction. The sensitivity of a colour reaction refers to the minimum quantity of a substance which must be present in the path of the light beam, for the colour of the solution to be observable.

If we assume that the Bouguer–Lambert–Beer law

$$E = kcl \tag{8}$$

where E is the extinction; k the extinction coefficient; c the concentration of the substance in the solution; l the depth of coloured solution, remains valid for infinitesimally small quantities of a substance, then we should speak of the minimum concentration for a given reaction only with respect to a given depth of solution, if the concept of "minimum concentration" is to have a definite meaning.

For a given coloured substance ($k = $ const.), the product $c \times l = E$ is a constant, from which it follows that the magnitude of the minimum concentration is determined by the nature of the coloured substance and the length of light path chosen: it does not depend on any other quantities, in particular, not on the cross-section of the column of fluid.

The other factor determining the sensitivity of a reaction is the minimum detectable amount m, defined by

$$m = c_{min} \times v. \tag{6}$$

But $v = ls$, where l is the depth of the layer of coloured solution and s the cross-section of the column of liquid. Hence

$$m = c_{min} \times l \times s,$$

i.e., the minimum detectable amount is proportional to the cross-section of the column of liquid.

In ultramicroanalysis, coloriscopic capillaries (described below) are used for observing colour. In these the depth of the layer of solution is commensurate with that in macroanalysis, but the cross-section is very much smaller, thus allowing a considerable reduction in the minimum detectable amount. The cross-section of a column in ultramicroanalysis is generally 10^4 times smaller than in macroanalysis, the detectable minima being in the same ratio to one another.

The minimum concentration, however, which does not depend on the cross-section of the column of liquid, is identical for macroanalysis and ultramicroanalysis for commensurate depths of solution if related to unit depth.

The colour intensity of solutions observed under the microscope may be characterized by the Bouguer–Lambert–Beer law [33].

Putting $k = $ const. and knowing that

$$c = \frac{m}{v} \quad \text{and} \quad l = \frac{v}{s},$$

where m is the absolute mass of a substance; v the volume of solution; s the cross-section of the column of solution, we obtain

$$E = cl = \frac{m}{v} \times \frac{v}{s}; \quad E = \frac{m}{s} \tag{9}$$

This is valid for the cross-section area of the column of coloured solution itself, but not for its magnified image under the microscope. For the intensity of the colour to remain unchanged with magnification of its image, the intensity of the light used for illumination must be increased correspondingly.

Apparatus

Observation of the colour of solutions in small volumes presents considerable difficulties; frequently the colour is quite imperceptible owing to the thinness of the layer of solution (in the vessels used in ultramicroanalysis the depth of solution is 0·5–2·0 mm).

The coloriscopic capillary permits a large increase in the depth of solution without any change in volume. The capillary is a piece of glass tube some 5–15 mm long with a capillary channel 0·2–0·5 mm

DUCTS IN COLORISCOPIC CAPILLARIES

olour in illary	Minimum detectable, g		Minimum concentration		Macromethod (height of column of solution 1 cm)	
	Height of column of solution 1 cm	For the given height of solution	Height of column of solution 1 cm	For the given height of solution	Detectable minimum, g	Minimum concentration
Red ↓ Pink None	1.5×10^{-9}	2×10^{-9}	$1:880,000$	$1:500,000$	10^{-5}	$1:100,000$
Pink None	1.5×10^{-9}	1×10^{-9}	$1:880,000$	$1:1,000,000$	10^{-5}	$1:100,000$
ight blue None	0.75×10^{-9}	1×10^{-9}	$1:1,750,000$	$1:1,000,000$	10^{-6}	$1:1,000,000$
iolet ↓ ight lac	2.25×10^{-12}	3×10^{-12}	$1:590,000,000$	$1:330,000,000$	10^{-8}	$1:50,000,000$

in the cone with the pipette tip. Rinse the pipette several times with distilled water and use it to add to the microcone a measured volume of potassium thiocyanate solution.

Take as much nitric acid as will ensure that the acidity of the final volume is not less than 0·05 N; the amount of potassium thiocyanate is calculated from the requirement that its final concentration in the solution is about 0·3 M. Transfer the solution prepared to the coloriscopic capillary and observe the pinkish colour under the microscope.

The final concentration of iron in the solution prepared can be calculated from the overall volume of solution in the microcone and the quantity of iron (III) chloride in it. On the basis of this concentration and the volume of the coloriscopic capillary, which can easily be calculated from the given height and diameter of the capillary channel, calculate the absolute mass of the substance to be determined in the form of a coloured complex.

The data obtained in this way are given in Tables 6 and 7.

The Detection of Cobalt in the Form of Thiocyanate

Prepare a solution of cobalt chloride $\left(0\cdot1 \dfrac{m\gamma}{m\lambda} \text{Co}\right)$ and a 50 per cent solution of ammonium thiocyanate. Chemically pure acetone is also required.

In the holder in the moist chamber place two microvessels and one microcone about 1·5 mm in diameter, and also one microvessel about 0·5 mm in diameter. Place the coloriscopic capillary on the cover slip on the chamber lid in the special round chamber.

Fill one of the 1·5 mm vessels with the ammonium thiocyanate solution and the 0·5 mm vessel with cobalt chloride solution.

Pipette a measured volume of cobalt chloride solution into the microcone, wash the pipette several times in distilled water and then transfer a measured volume of ammonium thiocyanate to the microcone: mix the solution.

Again wash the pipette and use it to fill the second 1·5 mm vessel with acetone. At once take the necessary quantity of acetone from the vessel, transfer it to the cone and mix.

The concentration of ammonium thiocyanate in the final volume of solution should be not less than 5 per cent and the acetone concentration not less than 50 per cent.

Transfer the prepared solution to the capillary by the method described above. Observe the blue colour of the solution in the microscope.

The data obtained on the detection of cobalt by this method are given in Table 6.

The Detection of Chromium by Means of Diphenylcarbazide

Prepare a solution of potassium chromate $\left(0\cdot001 \dfrac{m\gamma}{m\lambda} \text{Cr}\right)$, a 6 N solution of sulphuric acid and a 0·25 per cent solution of diphenylcarbazide in a mixture of acetone and water (1:1).

In the moist chamber on the holder place three vessels and one microcone about 1·5 mm in diameter, one vessel 0·5 mm in diameter and a measuring capillary with an approximate diameter of 0·1 mm.

Put a coloriscopic capillary on a cover slip on the lid of the chamber.

Use a pipette to fill one of the 1·5 mm vessels with distilled water and a second with 6 N sulphuric acid solution. Fill the 0·5 mm vessel with potassium chromate solution. The measuring capillary in this case serves for measuring out the potassium chromate solution, because, in view of the high sensitivity of the reaction, very small volumes of this solution have to be measured.

Transfer to the microcone by pipette measured volumes of distilled water, sulphuric acid and potassium chromate, and mix. Wash the pipette several times with distilled water and then use it to fill the third 1·5 mm vessel with the diphenylcarbazide solution: at once take the quantity required from this vessel, transfer it to the cone and mix. The sulphuric acid concentration in the final volume should be about 0·1 N.

Transfer the solution prepared in the cone to the coloriscopic capillary and observe in the microscope the violet (to light blue) colour of the solution.

The data provided by this method are given in Table 6.

Conclusion

The experimental data confirm our theoretical analysis. Thus, we see that:

(i) the minimum detectable amount depends on the cross-section area of the column of coloured solution. Thus, in macroanalysis, where the cross-section is 1 cm², the minimum detectable amount of iron, for example, is 10^{-5} g, while it is 10^{-9} g in ultramicroanalysis;

(ii) the minimum detectable amount depends on the depth of the layer of solution; and

(iii) the minimum concentration, referred to unit length, according to the data of Table 6, is different in ultramicroanalysis from macroanalysis. The difference, however, is not large, whereas the minimum detectable amounts differ by several orders.

The data in Table 6 refer to columns of solution of equal cross-section.

If columns of unequal cross-section are used for observation, the Bouguer–Lambert–Beer law is seen not to hold. This failure of the law is related to the physiological characteristics of the eye: under identical conditions of observation, a column of solution of greater cross-section of the same concentration appears to be more intensely coloured, and, correspondingly, the colour, which is not visible in a column of smaller cross-section, may be detected by the eye.

This effect is particularly pronounced in ultramicroanalysis, where capillaries are used whose diameters differ by two, three, four or even more times. The effect is illustrated in Table 7.

THE FORMATION AND OBSERVATION OF PRECIPITATES

The reactions used in the method of determination by precipitation are normally done in microcones. The manipulations required (measuring out of a definite volume of solution, its transfer to the cone, the addition of the reagent, mixing and centrifugation) are described in detail by Benedetti-Pichler [33].

We, therefore, give below only examples of the detection of a number of elements that form various precipitates, without dwelling on the details of the techniques involved.

Detection and Separation by Precipitation

The Precipitation of Silver Chloride

Prepare solutions of silver nitrate $\left(10 \frac{m\gamma}{m\lambda} \text{ Ag}\right)$ and potassium chloride $\left(10 \frac{m\gamma}{m\lambda} \text{ Cl}^-\right)$.

Calculate the quantities of solution needed to produce a silver chloride precipitate weighing about 100 $m\gamma$.

Place in the moist chamber three microvessels, two measuring capillaries and one capillary cone. Fill one of the vessels with distilled water, a second with the potassium chloride solution and the third with silver nitrate solution. Using a pipette, extract about 10 $m\lambda$ of silver nitrate solution, measure out this volume exactly in one of the measuring

TABLE 7. THE OBSERVATION OF THE COLOUR OF SOLUTIONS IN CAPILLARIES OF DIFFERENT CROSS-SECTION

Element	Reagents	Capillary dimensions			Absolute mass of element, g		Minimum detectable, g		Minimum concentration	
		Diameter, mm	Length, mm	Volume, mm^3	In prepared solution	In capillary	Height of column of solution 1 cm	For the given height of column	Height of column of solution 1 cm	For the given height of column
Iron	Potassium thiocyanate	0·82	7·5	4·0	$2 \cdot 5 \times 10^{-9}$	2×10^{-9}	$1 \cdot 5 \times 10^{-9}$	2×10^{-9}	1:3,500,000	1:2,000,000
		0·41	7·5	1·0	6×10^{-9}	2×10^{-9}	$1 \cdot 5 \times 10^{-9}$	2×10^{-9}	1:880,000	1:500,000

capillaries and pipette it into the cone. Dilute the solution twice with water. Wash out the pipette and use it to transfer to the cone about 5 mλ of potassium chloride solution taken from the vessel and measured in the other measuring capillary. Hereupon a silver chloride precipitate is formed. Mix the contents of the cone with the tip of the pipette. Remove the pipette from the moist chamber. Place the cone with the precipitate in a capillary and centrifuge.

The white colour of the precipitate and its structure are easily observed in reflected light.

The Precipitation of Barium Sulphate

Prepare solutions of barium chloride $\left(10 \frac{m\gamma}{m\lambda} Ba \right)$ and potassium sulphate $\left(10 \frac{m\gamma}{m\lambda} SO_4^{2-} \right)$.

Calculate the volumes of solution needed to produce about 50 mγ of barium sulphate precipitate.

Assemble the piston attachment and the necessary apparatus in the moist chamber.

Calculation shows that about 3 mλ of barium chloride solution and 2·5 mλ of potassium sulphate solution should be transferred to the cone for precipitation.

Precipitate exactly as in the previous experiment. Observe the clouding of the solution in reflected light. Collect all the precipitate at the apex of the cone by prolonged centrifugation: for this place the cone with the precipitate in a capillary with a droplet of water in it and sealed at both ends.

The barium sulphate precipitate is especially clearly seen when viewed in monochromatic light (green, red or blue).

The Precipitation of Nickel Dimethylglyoxime

Prepare a solution of a nickel salt $\left(10 \frac{m\gamma}{m\lambda} Ni \right)$, a 1 per cent solution of dimethylglyoxime, nitric acid (1 : 1) and concentrated ammonium hydroxide.

Calculate the quantity of each solution needed to produce 50 mγ of precipitate.

In the moist chamber place four vessels, two measuring capillaries and one cone. Fill the vessels with the solutions: in each of the measuring capillaries respectively measure out a definite volume of the nickel salt solution or dimethylglyoxime solution; precipitate in the cone. Pipette about 1 mλ of the nickel salt solution into the cone, dilute twice with nitric acid, add 5 mλ of dimethylglyoxime solution and then ammonia solution until red flakes of precipitate appear. Wash out the pipette each time before using it for a different solution. Collect the precipitate in the apex of the cone by centrifugation (Fig. 19).

Thanks to its bright colour and large volume the precipitate is very easily seen in incident light. It is easily reprecipitated by dissolving in

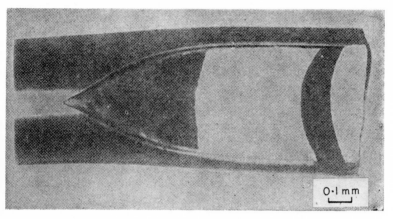

FIG. 19. Nickel dimethylglyoxime precipitate in a microcone.

nitric acid, evaporating and then adding dimethylglyoxime and ammonium hydroxide.

The Precipitation of Hydrous Iron (III) Oxide by Gaseous Ammonia

Prepare a solution of an iron salt $\left(10 \dfrac{m\gamma}{m\lambda} \text{ Fe}\right)$.

Calculate the volume of solution needed to produce 100 mγ of hydrous iron (III) oxide.

Place two vessels, a measuring capillary and a cone in the moist chamber. Transfer into the cone by pipette a measured volume (about 5 mλ) of the iron salt solution and dilute with water. Take the cone with the solution out of the chamber and place it in a capillary that has been bent at an oblique angle; then connect the capillary by rubber tubing to the vessel with the concentrated ammonium hydroxide (see p. 23) and blow air through. After a few minutes, extract the cone from the capillary and place it in another capillary for centrifugation. Then observe the typical precipitate of hydrous iron (III) oxide under the microscope.

The Separation of Copper and Iron by Means of Gaseous Ammonia

In the presence of excess of ammonium hydroxide, iron is precipitated in the form of the hydrous oxide, while copper remains in solution, forming a complex salt. By the subsequent separation of the solution from the precipitate and separate treatment of each with acid, it is possible to detect the presence of iron and copper ions in the solutions obtained by means of potassium ferrocyanide.

Prepare solutions of salts of iron $\left(10 \, \dfrac{m\gamma}{m\lambda} \, \text{Fe} \right)$ and copper $\left(10 \dfrac{m\gamma}{m\lambda} \, \text{Cu} \right)$ and a 2 per cent solution of potassium ferrocyanide.

In the moist chamber place four vessels (for the prepared solutions and for distilled water), two capillaries (for measuring the iron and copper solutions) and two cones (for the reactions).

Into one of the cones pipette $2 \cdot 5 \, m\lambda$ of iron salt solution and $3 \cdot 5 \, m\lambda$ of copper salt solution, these being calculated to produce $50 \, m\gamma$ of the respective hydroxides. Dilute twice with distilled water and treat the contents of the cone with gaseous ammonia until the blue colour of the copper complex appears. Centrifuge, separate the solution from the precipitate and transfer the solution to the other cone. To the hydrous iron oxide precipitate add 15–$20 \, m\lambda$ of distilled water and treat with hydrogen chloride (the gas is produced in the apparatus for use with gaseous reagents by pouring in concentrated hydrochloric acid and blowing air through), whereupon the precipitate is dissolved. To the iron (III) chloride solution thus obtained add the requisite volume of potassium ferrocyanide by measuring directly from the vessel, and observe the formation of the blue precipitate.

Destroy the copper–ammonia complex with hydrochloric acid, which is to be taken up into a micropipette from a cone with a bent stem. Judge the quantity of acid added by the increase in the volume of precipitate in the cone. Measuring directly from the vessel, take up into the pipette the necessary volume of potassium ferrocyanide solution and add it to the copper salt solution in the cone. On centrifugation, a voluminous brown precipitate collects at the apex of the cone.

The Separation and Detection of Lithium and Potassium

If solutions of salts of lithium and potassium are mixed, lithium phosphate can be precipitated out of solution, while the potassium remaining in the solution can be detected by means of sodium cobaltinitrite.

The normal way of carrying out this analysis calls for solutions of salts of lithium $\left(1 \, \dfrac{m\gamma}{m\lambda} \, \text{Li} \right)$ and potassium $\left(1 \, \dfrac{m\gamma}{m\lambda} \, \text{K} \right)$, a $0 \cdot 2 \, \text{N}$

solution of disodium hydrogen phosphate, a 25 per cent solution of ammonium hydroxide, a solution of sodium cobaltinitrite (0·5 g salt in 3 ml water) and ethyl alcohol.

In the moist chamber place six vessels (for the solutions and alcohol listed above), two measuring capillaries (for measuring out the solutions of salts of lithium and potassium) and two cones.

Measure out the necessary volumes of the solutions directly in the vessels. To obtain 25 mγ of lithium phosphate and 10 mγ of potassium sodium cobaltinitrite, transfer to the cone about 5 mλ of a lithium salt solution and about 2 mλ of potassium salt solution.

Add ammonium hydroxide, then the solution of disodium hydrogen phosphate and the alcohol. Heat the contents of the cone with a micro-heater, and centrifuge, whereupon the white precipitate of lithium phosphate comes down. Separate the solution from the precipitate, transfer it to the other cone and add the sodium cobaltinitrite solution. Observe the formation of the yellow precipitate.

Semi-quantitative Determination by Volume of Precipitate

If the volumes of the precipitates obtained in the course of the analysis are determined, it is possible to establish approximately the quantity of an element in the solution, and also the ratio between the various components in the solution.

The essence of the method is that, under identical conditions, the experimentalist produces side by side and collects by centrifugation in the apices of the respective cones, the precipitates of the solution under analysis and a standard solution, measures the parameters of the precipitates obtained and calculates their volumes. The quantity of the element in question in the precipitate formed from the standard solution being known, it is possible to calculate the quantity in the solution being examined.

Benedetti-Pichler [33] suggests that the volume of a cone of regular section should be calculated, the cone taken being a fictitious one such that it contains the precipitate (Fig. 20, 1). Its volume is equal to the difference of the volumes of two cones of heights H and h and base diameters D and d, i.e.,

$$v = v_1 - v_2 = \frac{\pi}{3}\left(\frac{D}{2}\right)^2 H - \frac{\pi}{3}\left(\frac{d}{2}\right)^2 h = 0\cdot26(D^2 H - d^2 h) \qquad (10)$$

A simpler way of obtaining no less accurate data is to collect the precipitates formed carefully in the apex of the vessel, so that a right cone is formed (Fig. 20, 2), whose volume is given by the formula:

$$v = 0.26 D^2 H \tag{11}$$

The results are more reproducible with compact precipitates where

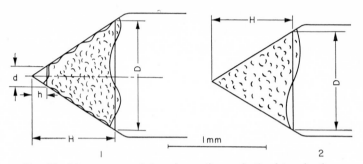

FIG. 20. Measurement of the volume of cones in the determination of an element by the volume of precipitate.

the crystals are small. The conditions of precipitation are also significant.

It should be noted that the external picture does not always characterize exactly the structure of the precipitate. Thus, tungsten can be determined accurately enough by the volume of the gelatinous precipitate of tungstic acid [41]. On the other hand, iron can be determined accurately enough by the volume of its hydrous oxide precipitate, but not by the volume of the ferrocyanide.

On the other hand, the crystalline precipitate of lead chloride is not suitable for the determination of lead by the volume of precipitate, because the crystals are large and therefore do not pack sufficiently compactly, so that their density when collected at the apex of the cone is not always uniform. Silver may be determined in the form of its chloride, provided that the precipitate is not heated before centrifugation; otherwise considerable variations are found in parallel determinations. Clearly, the possibility of determining by volume of precipitate in the form of a certain compound is best ascertained experimentally. Below we give the methods and results for the semi-quantitative determination of a number of elements [41].

The Determination of Lead

Treat 50 mλ of a solution containing about 0·5 γ lead with an approximately equal volume of a concentrated solution of potassium chromate. Centrifuge the contents of the cone simultaneously with a standard precipitate and measure the volumes of the precipitate.

The following series of numbers is obtained (the volume of precipitate is expressed in mλ/γ of lead):

$$28 \quad 28 \quad 30 \quad 32 \quad 32 \quad 32 \quad 32 \quad 34 \quad 34$$

Mean value	32 mλ/γ
Mean deviation	±2 mλ/γ
Error	7%

The Determination of Univalent Mercury

Treat 50 mλ of a solution containing about 0·5 γ mercury with an approximately equal volume of 5 N hydrochloric acid in a cone. Centrifuge the contents of the cone without heating, whereupon the fine crystals of the white precipitate are forced into a compact mass at the apex of the cone. Measure the diameter and height of this mass.

The following series of figures is obtained:

$$9·0 \quad 9·4 \quad 9·6 \quad 10·4 \quad 10·8 \quad 11·2 \quad 11·4 \quad 12·2 \quad 12·4 \quad 12·8$$

Mean value	10·9 mλ/γ
Mean deviation	±1·3 mλ/γ
Error	12%

The Determination of Silver

Treat 5 mλ of a solution containing about 0·5 γ silver with approximately the same volume of 5 N hydrochloric acid in a cone. Centrifuge without heating. Measure the diameter and height of the precipitate and calculate its volume:

$$11·4 \quad 11·8 \quad 11·8 \quad 12·2 \quad 13·8 \quad 14·2 \quad 14·6 \quad 15·8 \quad 16$$

Mean value	13·4 mλ/γ
Mean deviation	±1·7 mλ/γ
Error	13%

The Determination of Tungsten

Tungsten can be determined well in the form of tungstic acid, especially after its reprecipitation out of ammonia solution.

Treat 50 mλ of a solution of tungstate with an approximately equal volume of 5 N hydrochloric acid, heat for five minutes up to almost 100° and centrifuge. Determine the volume of precipitate (series 1).

5

Dissolve the precipitate obtained in $50\,m\lambda$ ammonium hydroxide (specific gravity 0·88), mixing the while. Then add 5 N hydrochloric or nitric acid until precipitation is complete, heat and centrifuge. Calculate the volume of precipitate (series II).

Series I	14·4	14·4	15·8	16·0	16·0	17·4	17·6	17·9	19·6	19·6
	HCl	HCl	HNO_3	HCl	HCl	HCl	HNO_3	HNO_3	HCl	HCl
Series II	13·8	14·4	15·4	15·0	15·8	15·4	17·0	17·6	17·6	18·4

	Series I	Series II
Mean value	16·8	$16\cdot1\ m\lambda/\gamma$
Mean deviation	±1·9	$\pm1\cdot5\ m\lambda/\gamma$
Error	11	9%

The Determination of Vanadium

When vanadium is precipitated in the form of lead vanadate, a voluminous orange precipitate comes down which packs well in the apex of the cone.

Acidify 50 mλ of solution with 10 mλ 2 N acetic acid. Then add 60–70 mλ of a neutral solution of lead acetate (twice diluted saturated aqueous solution), mix and centrifuge. Calculate the volume of precipitate.

In ten determinations the following data were obtained:

106 108 110 110 112 116 118 118 124 124

Mean value	$115\ m\lambda/\gamma$
Mean deviation	$\pm6\ m\lambda/\gamma$
Error	5%

By comparison with the preceding determination, greater accuracy is obtained here, evidently because a sufficiently bulky precipitate is formed.

The Determination of Potassium

Potassium is determined conveniently by the volume of precipitate in the form of cobaltinitrite, which is a voluminous precipitate of fine crystals.

Treat 100 mλ of a solution containing potassium with 50 mλ of a reagent, leave to stand for 30 min, centrifuge and measure the parameters of the precipitate.

The following data are obtained:

53   60   62   65   68   70

Mean value	$64\ m\lambda/\gamma$
Mean deviation	$\pm4\ m\lambda/\gamma$
Error	6%

MICROCRYSTALLINE REACTIONS*

In ultramicroanalysis, microcrystalline reactions are done on the illuminated surface of the condenser rod, the quantities of solution required being 1–3 mλ in all with a content of 5–10 mγ of the ion to be detected.

The technique used is the following.

Manipulate a pipette with a measured quantity of solution into such a position that it occupies a third of the field of view of the microscope. Whilst observing with the naked eye, use the movable stage to bring up to the tip of the pipette the flat surface of the condenser rod; focus the microscope.

With the manipulator bring the pipette tip into sharp focus. Direct a beam of light on to the section F of the rod, which is turned towards the rear wall of the chamber; thereupon the platform is brilliantly illuminated, while the rest of the field of view remains dark. Now using reflected and incident light simultaneously, manoeuvre the illuminated platform into the centre of the field of view with the aid of the movable stage. Bring the pipette tip right up to the illuminated platform with the manipulator. Again with the manipulator, raise the tip of the pipette slightly (hereupon its contours become less sharp) and move it horizontally until the aperture is over the surface of the platform. Then lower the tip carefully until it touches the platform, when its contours again become sharp. By turning the screw of the piston, force a drop of solution out of the pipette on to the platform; then raise the pipette and remove it from the moist chamber.

Wash the pipette several times with water from a cone, introducing its end into the cone with the manipulator. The water first enters the pipette of its own accord, then a certain quantity is sucked in by the piston. Then withdraw the pipette tip from the cone with the manipulator and expel the washing water from it.

Add a measured quantity of the necessary reagent to the solution on the platform of the condenser rod.

Measure the reagent with the calibrated tip of a micropipette (this is especially convenient for volumes of 1 mλ or less). (This is done by introducing the tip of the micropipette into the vessel with the reagent in such a way that the aperture of the pipette coincides with the far end of the scale of the eyepiece micrometer.) Allow the reagent to enter the pipette until the length of capillary corresponding to the given volume is filled. Transfer this to the platform in the same way as the solution under investigation.

* Useful information on chemical microscopy, including microcrystalline reactions, may be found in Chamot and Mason's book [70].

Before dipping the tip of the pipette with the reagent into the solution on the platform, create a slight pressure in the pipette by a clockwise rotation of the screw. In this way the reagent flows out of the pipette as soon as it touches the solution on the platform, and the latter does not enter the pipette.

View the precipitate formed with the condenser rod illuminated by transverse light and with various magnifications, depending on the character of the complex formed.

After one reaction has been done, the platform can be prepared for further use by the dissolution of the precipitate and subsequent washing of the platform with water. If this is not successful, a new platform can be obtained from the same condenser rod by nicking and breaking off the fibre just below the old platform. This can be repeated until the fibre is completely used up.

We give one example below. *The Determination of Silver in the Form of Bichromate.**

Prepare a solution of silver nitrate $\left(10 \frac{m\gamma}{m\lambda} \text{ Ag}\right)$ in 10 per cent nitric acid and a saturated solution of potassium dichromate.

In the moist chamber place two calibrated vessels, a measuring capillary and the condenser rod. Fill one of the vessels with the silver nitrate solution, the other with the potassium dichromate solution. Then take somewhat more than 1 mλ of silver nitrate solution from the first vessel with a pipette, measure 1 mλ exactly with the aid of the measuring capillary and transfer this by pipette on to the platform of the condenser rod. Wash the pipette several times with distilled water, then with potassium dichromate solution; draw from the appropriate vessel 1 mλ of this solution with the pipette, using the calibration data obtained with the silver nitrate solution. Transfer the measured quantity of potassium dichromate solution to the platform of the condenser rod. Observe the yellow crystals of silver dichromate formed in reflected light.

SYSTEMATIC QUALITATIVE ANALYSIS

The normal hydrogen sulphide scheme can be used for the qualitative investigation of small samples on the ultramicroscale. This technique involves treatment with hydrogen sulphide of a small volume of solution by saturating it with this gas. However, some of the reagents used in the normal technique must be changed. Thus, concentrated hydrochloric acid must be replaced by dilute

* Duval [71] provides information about several new microcrystalline reactions.

(1:1), because the concentrated acid gives off a vapour which may act on the sample as a gaseous reagent. On the other hand, the concentrated acid may also be used, if it is employed intentionally as a gaseous reagent. Lead chloride should not be dissolved in hot water, because the small volume of the water cools rapidly and the lead chloride reprecipitates. A good solvent to use in this case is ammonium acetate. It is undesirable to use ammonium poly-sulphide, because the tip of the pipette becomes blocked with sulphur.

At the same time Wilson and his colleagues [40–43] have developed part of a detailed analytical scheme for work on the ultramicroscale that avoids the hydrogen sulphide scheme; their full scheme was worked out for microanalysis [72].

The classification of elements into groups and the systematic procedure given below is that recommended by these workers.

Wilson's Analytical Scheme

Wilson's scheme is not, in our opinion, faultless. However, it is the only one worked out with the special features of ultramicro-analysis taken into account. We, therefore, consider it necessary to acquaint the reader with it.

Groups	I	II	III		IV	V	VI
			A	B			
Elements	Na	Pb	Ti	Pb	Ag Hg (II)	Cr Sn	Zn Mn
		Hg (I)	Zr	Ca	Cu Bi	Al Fe	V U
	K	Ag	Ge	Sr	Mo Sn	Mn Ti	Ni Co
		W	Th	Ba	Sb	Zr	Cd Mg

Group I ions are detected each from a separate portion of the solution; the systematic procedure proper starts with Group II.

Group II Analysis

In comparison with the microanalytical procedure, the authors recommend the following modifications in the method of analysing Group II:

(1) the use of hydrochloric acid diluted (1:1) instead of concentrated;

(2) the dissolution of lead chloride in a 10 per cent solution of ammonium acetate, not in hot water, when silver and tungsten remain in the precipitate;

(3) the use of a 5 per cent solution of potassium cyanide instead of ammonium hydroxide as solvent for silver chloride;

(4) the exclusion of mercury (I) from Group II on account of its oxidation to mercury (II) by the heating of the chloride precipitate; and

(5) the precipitation of vanadium in Group II, if it is not specially retained in solution.

The general analytical procedure for Group II is given below.

The reagents are 5 N hydrochloric acid, a 10 per cent solution of ammonium acetate and a 5 per cent solution of potassium cyanide.

Treat 50 mλ of a solution containing 0·5 γ of each element with an approximately equal volume of 5 N hydrochloric acid in a microcone. Seal the cone in a capillary, centrifuge and heat in an aluminium block to almost 100° for 5 min. Place the sealed capillary in cold water for 15 min; then take out the cone and transfer it to the holder in the chamber.

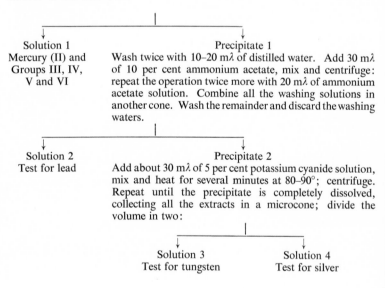

Solution 1
Mercury (II) and
Groups III, IV,
V and VI

Precipitate 1
Wash twice with 10–20 mλ of distilled water. Add 30 mλ of 10 per cent ammonium acetate, mix and centrifuge: repeat the operation twice more with 20 mλ of ammonium acetate solution. Combine all the washing solutions in another cone. Wash the remainder and discard the washing waters.

Solution 2
Test for lead

Precipitate 2
Add about 30 mλ of 5 per cent potassium cyanide solution, mix and heat for several minutes at 80–90°; centrifuge. Repeat until the precipitate is completely dissolved, collecting all the extracts in a microcone; divide the volume in two:

Solution 3
Test for tungsten

Solution 4
Test for silver

The Detection of Lead

(a) *Reaction with dithizone. Reagents:* 0·05 per cent solution of dithizone in carbon tetrachloride; saturated aqueous solution of potassium cyanide (free from lead); 10 per cent ammonium acetate solution.

Transfer 20 mλ of solution 2 to a cone, add some potassium cyanide solution and mix the contents of the cone with the tip of the pipette. Wash the pipette with water, then several times with ammonium acetate solution and finally with water again. Draw into the pipette about 20 mλ of dithizone solution. If the reagent changes colour at this stage, the pipette is not clean enough and must be re-washed. Otherwise, transfer the dithizone immediately to the microcone.

The presence of lead is detected by the red colour of the complex formed with the dithizone. In view of the especially high sensitivity of the reaction, particular care should be taken that the pipettes, cone, reagents and washing solutions are not contaminated with lead.

(b) *Reaction with potassium chromate.* Treat 20–30 mλ of the solution with an equal volume of saturated potassium chromate solution in a microcone, whereupon a yellow precipitate of lead chromate is formed.

This reaction may also be done on the illuminated platform of the condenser rod.

The Detection of Mercury (I)

Treat 20–30 mλ of the initial solution in a microcone with an approximately equal volume of 5 N hydrochloric acid. Centrifuge and place the cone in the holder in the chamber. Remove the supernatant liquid, wash the precipitate with 30 mλ of water, add about 30 mλ of concentrated ammonium hydroxide without mixing.

If there is mercury (I) present, the precipitate becomes dark grey or black, which can be seen clearly both in reflected and in incident light.

The Detection of Silver

Reagents: p-dimethylaminobenzalrhodanine, saturated solution in acetone; 2 N nitric acid.

The reaction is done on a cotton fibre.

Fix a fine fibre on a holder (see p. 21), feed it with a solution of the reagent and place it horizontally in the chamber. Then transfer to the fibre about 20 mλ of solution 4 and about 20 mλ of 2 N nitric acid.

If there is silver present, the fibre takes on a violet colour, which is readily visible in contrast to the orange colouring of the thread caused by the reagent. The colour is seen especially clearly in reflected light. Even clearer results can be obtained if the fibre is first fed with the silver solution, then with the reagent and finally with nitric acid.

The Detection of Tungsten

Transfer 20–30 mλ of solution 3 to the platform of the condenser rod and allow it to evaporate there. Then add an approximately equal volume of 25 per cent solution of stannic chloride in 10 N hydrochloric acid, covering the dry residue of the sample with this drop.

If tungsten is present, a blue precipitate is formed slowly, which is seen best if the base of the condenser rod is illuminated.

The Analysis of Group III

In passing from the micro- to the ultramicroscale, the authors introduce the following changes in the procedure for analysing Group III:

(1) titanium and zirconium are excluded from the group, because these elements are only partially precipitated by the group reagent. This part is redissolved and the elements identified in Group V;

(2) the sulphate precipitates are treated not with water, but with dilute hydrochloric acid, because the precipitates of cerium and thorium are only slightly soluble in water. The use of hydrochloric acid involves some change in the following parts of the analysis;

(3) calcium is precipitated with sodium carbonate, not ammonium carbonate; and

(4) barium sulphate is converted to carbonate by a longer treatment.

The general procedure for analysing Group III is given below.

Reagents: hydrochloride acid, 10 N, 5 N, 2 N; nitric acid, 2 N; ammonium hydroxide, 2 N; 10 per cent solution of ammonium acetate; 10 per cent solution of ammonium oxalate; 10 per cent solution of ammonium sulphate; ethyl alcohol; oxalic acid, saturated solution; sodium carbonate, saturated solution; sodium hydroxide, 2 N; sodium sulphate, saturated solution.

Evaporate the filtrate obtained after Group II down to its original volume. Add an equal volume of saturated sodium sulphate solution, then a volume of ethyl alcohol equal to the combined total. Heat to 60°. Cool and centrifuge. See further the scheme on p. 57.

The Detection of Lead

(a) *Reaction with potassium chromate.* Described above.

(b) *Reaction of forming a complex thiocyanate. Reagents:* 80 per cent

Precipitate 1
Treat twice with 5 N hydrochloric acid.

Solution 2
Add excess ammonium hydroxide, centrifuge.

Precipitate 3
Treat with a hot solution of ammonium acetate.

Precipitate 4
Dissolve in hot 2 N hydrochloric acid. Cool. Dilute with an equal volume of water. Add an equal amount of saturated oxalic acid solution. Mix and centrifuge.

Solution 1
Combine with solution 6.

Solution 6
Combine with solution 1.

Groups IV, V, VI

Precipitate 6
Wash with dilute oxalic acid containing some nitric acid. Discard the washing fluid. Treat for 5 min with sodium hydroxide at 80° and centrifuge.

Solution 8
Discard.

Precipitate 8
Wash with water. Dissolve in hot 2 N nitric acid. Divide in two portions.

Part 1
Test for cerium.

Part 2
Test for thorium.

Solution 3
Add ammonium sulphate and ammonium oxalate solutions: heat to 100°, cool and centrifuge.

Solution 4
Combine with solution 5.

Solution 5
Combine with solution 4.
Evaporate to dryness and dissolve the dry residue in water. Test for lead.

Precipitate 5
Combine with precipitate 2.

Precipitate 2
Combine with precipitate 5.
Treat with saturated sodium carbonate solution for 10 min in a sealed capillary at 100°; centrifuge.

Solution 7
Discard.

Precipitate 7
Wash, dissolve in 2 N nitric acid and evaporate to dryness. Treat twice with alcohol.

Solution 9
Evaporate to dryness. Dissolve the residue in water. Treat for calcium.

Precipitate 9
Evaporate twice to dryness with 10 N hydrochloric acid. Treat with alcohol.

Solution 10
Evaporate to dryness. Dissolve the residue in water. Test for strontium.

Precipitate 10
Dissolve in water. Test for barium.

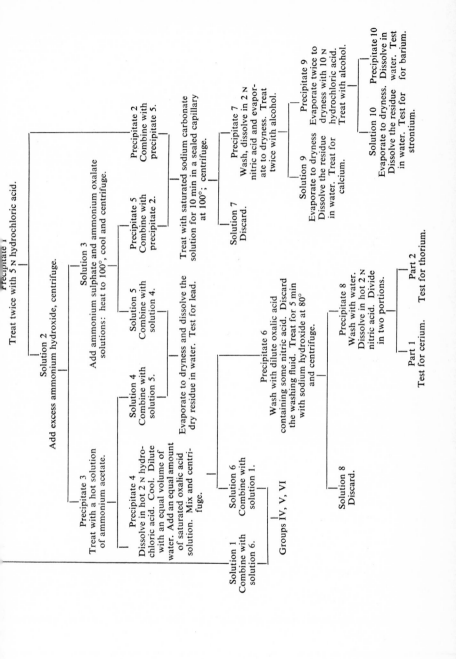

solution of potassium thiocyanate; 25 per cent solution of potassium mercurithiocyanate; zinc sulphate, saturated solution.

Treat 20–30 mλ of solutions 4 and 5, combined in a microcone, with 10–15 mλ of potassium thiocyanate solution, then with small amounts of the potassium mercurithiocyanate and zinc sulphate solutions. If there is lead present, a yellow precipitate is formed. If the sample is lead-free, a white precipitate is obtained.

The Detection of Calcium

(a) *Reaction with ammonium oxalate.* To 25 mλ of solution 9 add some saturated ammonium oxalate solution in a microcone. The presence of calcium is indicated by the appearance of a white precipitate.

(b) *Reaction with potassium ferrocyanide.* Transfer 25 mλ of solution 9 to a microcone containing some crystals of ammonium chloride. Add a small volume of a saturated solution of potassium ferrocyanide and observe the appearance of a white precipitate.

The Detection of Strontium

(a) *Reaction with sodium rhodizonate. Reagents:* sodium rhodizonate, a freshly prepared 1 per cent solution; 0·1 N hydrochloric acid.

Soak a piece of filter paper with the sodium rhodizonate. Transfer to the paper 25 mλ of solution 10 and place the paper on the holder in the moist chamber. Under the microscope observe a red-brown spot, which disappears when the paper is treated with dilute hydrochloric acid.

(b) *Reaction with potassium dichromate. Reagents:* acetic acid, 2 N; 10 per cent solution of potassium dichromate.

Acidify 25 mλ of solution 10 in a microcone with the acetic acid. Add the potassium dichromate solution and then ammonia solution. If there is strontium present, a precipitate will appear after the addition of ammonium hydroxide.

The Detection of Barium

(a) *Reaction with sodium rhodizonate.* This reaction is done as described above for strontium with solution 10. If the red-brown colour does not disappear when the paper is treated with hydrochloric acid, there is barium present.

(b) *Reaction with potassium dichromate.* Proceed as in the case of strontium above, using solution 10 but not adding ammonium hydroxide. If barium is present, a yellow precipitate is formed.

The Detection of Cerium

(a) *Reaction with hydrogen peroxide.* Transfer 25 mλ of the solution of precipitate 8 into a microcone, add some hydrogen peroxide (30 per cent) and make alkaline with ammonium hydroxide.

If cerium is present, a yellow-brown precipitate is formed.

(*b*) *Reaction with benzidine.* *Reagents:* sodium hydroxide, 2 N; benzidine (dissolve 0·05 g benzidine in 10 ml of ice-cold acetic acid and dilute to 100 ml with water).

Soak a piece of filter paper with sodium hydroxide solution. Then transfer to the paper 25 mλ of the solution of precipitate 8 and an equal volume of the benzidine solution. Observe in the microscope the formation of a blue spot, which denotes the presence of cerium.

The Detection of Thorium

(*a*) *Reaction with potassium iodate.* Place 25 mλ of the solution of precipitate 8 in a microcone and add twice this volume of concentrated nitric acid, then a similar volume of a saturated solution of potassium iodate. If thorium is present, a white precipitate is formed.

(*b*) *Reaction with alizarin.* Centrifuge the iodate precipitate and wash with a dilute solution of potassium iodate containing nitric acid. Add to the cone 100 mλ of hydrochloric acid and evaporate to dryness. Dissolve the remnant in 50 mλ of water. Transfer this solution to a piece of filter paper and add a drop of 1 per cent solution of alizarin in alcohol. The formation of a violet spot confirms the presence of thorium.

On the Analysis of Groups IV, V and VI

The scheme avoiding the use of hydrogen sulphide for ultramicroanalysis is modified for Groups II and III, as can be seen from the material adduced above. The full analytical scheme is worked out in detail in the original work [72] for use on the microscale. Until there are further developments, the same source can be used to obtain the necessary general information on the analysis of Groups IV, V and VI.

CHAPTER IV

METHODS OF SEPARATION

SEPARATION BY PRECIPITATION

SEPARATION by precipitation is, as is well known, the simplest
method of separation. Under certain determinate conditions, the
desired component is separated as a precipitate and is thus isolated
from the accompanying elements. Thus, two operations are required
—the production of a precipitate and its separation from the solution.
These operations present no special difficulty on the ultramicroscale;
they are described in the section "The formation and observation
of precipitates", where relevant examples are given.

SEPARATION BY ELECTROLYSIS

Thanks to the simplicity and speed of the operation, the electrolytic separation of metals from solution is an excellent method of
isolating the elements. Particularly useful is the method of separating
elements on a mercury cathode.

With the aid of special apparatus, electrolysis may also be done
under the microscope. The minimum amount of metal in solution
for electrolytic separation to be possible can be determined by means
of Nernst's equation. The calculation for copper ions gives the
following result. The potential required to separate copper from a
normal solution is 0·34 V. The overvoltage of hydrogen on copper
is 0·23 V, i.e., the separation potential is $-0·23$ V, so that the cathode
potential may be brought as low as this value. At such a potential
the concentration of copper ions in solution, according to Nernst's
formula, is

$$-0·23 = 0·34 - \frac{0·058}{2} \log \frac{1}{C} \tag{12}$$

$$0·57 = 0·29 \log \frac{1}{C}, \quad \text{whence} \quad C \simeq 10^{-20}$$

This concentration lies beyond the limits of any qualitative determination.

To separate any element electrolytically, a definite set of conditions must be established. The electrode voltage must be not less than the decomposition potential of the solution analysed. The surface area of the electrodes used in ultramicroanalysis is small; further, a definite current density $(0\cdot10-0\cdot01\ A/cm^2)$ must be maintained. It is, therefore, necessary to use a current of 10^{-4} to 10^{-5} A.

Electrolysis with Platinum Electrodes

Platinum electrodes have the advantage that they ensure the absence of any contamination of the solution by foreign ions during electrolysis. They are therefore preferred in ultramicro-analysis to solid electrodes made from other materials.

Apparatus

The electrolytic separation of metals from small volumes is achieved by the use of special apparatus [44], differing from that used on the macroscale in the part directly involved in the process. The general pattern remains substantially unchanged: the current is supplied to the electrolytic cell from an accumulator (a source of constant current and voltage 4–6 V) via a plug resistance box. The necessary voltage is applied and a definite, known resistance (obtained by using the plug box) is inserted in the circuit: the necessary current density is thus obtained. The voltage between the terminals of the resistance box is monitored by a voltmeter.

The cells used in electrolysis with platinum electrodes may be of two types.

1. The solution to be electrolysed is placed on the end of a thick-walled capillary (external diameter about 5 mm and internal about $0\cdot5$ mm), shaped like a condenser rod (Fig. 21, 1). Into the channel of this capillary is fused a platinum wire about $0\cdot2$ mm in diameter; the end of this wire, which lies in the plane of the end of the capillary, serves as the anode (cathode). To the other end of this

wire, outside the capillary, is soldered a thin and flexible lead suitable for making connexion with the current source.

The cathode (anode) also consists of a platinum wire (Fig. 21, 2), soldered to a lead which passes through a capillary and an ebonite holder to a terminal, where it is connected to the circuit.

2. The solution to be electrolysed is placed in an ordinary micro-cone, into which the platinum electrodes are introduced. These

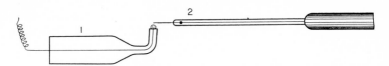

FIG. 21. Electrolysis on the condenser rod: 1—condenser rod electrode (anode); 2—cathode (anode).

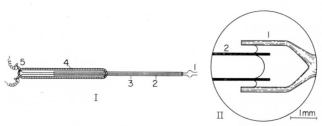

FIG. 22. Platinum fork electrodes: I—general view; II—view under the microscope.

electrodes consist of platinum wires, 0·1–0·2 mm in diameter, which are fused into capillaries and electrically isolated from one another (Fig. 22, II). The current is carried through thin wires which are soldered to the platinum wires.

Such electrodes are made as follows (Fig. 22, I). Take two platinum wires (1) of the requisite length (1–1·5 mm) and join them to two wires (2) with tin solder. Solder the wires in their turn to the terminals on the ebonite holder (4). Now place glass capillaries (3) over the wires, leaving the ends of the platinum wires free. Finally bend these ends as shown in Fig. 22, I.

Procedure

Electrolysis on the condenser rod. Fix the condenser-rod electrode on plasticine in the moist chamber, passing the lead through an aperture drilled in the rear wall of the chamber. Also place in the chamber a holder with the necessary additional vessels.

Fix the other electrode by its ebonite holder in the jaws of the left manipulator. In the right manipulator fix the piston attachment with a pipette. Place the light source at such a level that the light falls on the plane F of the condenser rod (see Fig. 9). With the apparatus so arranged, proceed to the electrolysis proper.

Fill the vessels in the chamber with the necessary solutions. Then with the pipette withdraw a definite quantity of one of the solutions and transfer it to the plane surface of the condenser electrode, bringing the latter into the field of view and focusing the microscope on it. Whilst observing both with the naked eye and through the microscope, bring the cathode up to the illuminated surface of the condenser rod and position it above the surface not touching the solution. Then connect the accumulator to the cell. Lower the left manipulator, thus introducing the cathode into the drop on the surface and closing the circuit. Hereupon the process of electrolysis begins; it may be observed conveniently under the microscope (bubbles of gas can be seen).

Determine the end of the process by the negative reaction of the solution to the relevant reagent. Perform this reaction on the illuminated surface of an ordinary condenser rod by transferring a small quantity of solution from the electrolytic surface and then adding the necessary reagent.

When the electrolysis is complete, break the circuit by raising the cathode with the manipulator and thus taking it out of the solution.

Then disconnect the current source.

The metal separated out is detected either by its characteristic colour or by dissolving it and detecting it in solution with the relevant reagent.

Electrolysis in a microcone. Place in the moist chamber the number of vessels needed for the solutions, and a microcone which is to serve as the electrolyser. The microcone must be of such diameter that, when the electrodes are immersed in the solution, they are a definite distance from the walls of the vessel. If the electrodes almost touch the walls of the vessel, then the solution forced out on their immersion spills over the walls of the vessel and so a part of the solution is not subjected to electrolysis. The length of the electrolyser must not exceed 4–5 mm; in this case only a small part of the electrodes is in the part not filled with solution, which constitutes about a third of the whole volume.

Clamp the chamber with the vessels on the microscope stage. Push the platinum wire electrodes into the left manipulator and the piston attachment with pipette into the right.

Use the pipette to transfer from the vessels to the electrolyser a measured volume of solution such that not more than two-thirds of the volume of the vessel is filled, to avoid losses caused by spraying out of the solution during electrolysis. Then turn the open side of the chamber to the left manipulator and, observing first with the naked eye, and then through the microscope, introduce the electrodes into the electrolyser without letting them dip into the solution. Connect the current source up to the electrodes; then dip the electrodes into the solution by moving the electrolyser on to them and thus closing the circuit.

Hereupon the process of electrolysis begins. It may be observed conveniently under the microscope (when gas bubbles will be seen), the end of the process being judged as described above.

When the electrolysis is completed, break the circuit by taking the electrodes out of the vessel and then out of the chamber (using the manipulator); then disconnect the current source.

Detect the metal isolated by its characteristic colour, or dissolve it and detect in solution by means of the appropriate reagent.

Examples of the Electrolytic Separation of Metals

The separation of copper on a platinum cathode. Prepare a solution of copper sulphate $\left(1\,\dfrac{m\gamma}{m\lambda}\,Cu\right)$ containing 0·2 M sulphuric acid. Calculate the current needed on the basis of the surface area of the elements and the current density recommended (0·001–0·01 A/cm²). For the electrodes used, it will be 10^{-4} to 10^{-6} A. The voltage needed for electrolysing solutions of copper salts is generally 2·2 V.

Obtain the required current and voltage from an accumulator by introducing the required resistance on the plug box.

Electrolyse as described above, either on the illuminated surface of the condenser rod or in a microcone electrolyser. View the copper deposit formed on the cathode under a microscope in reflected light. If the layer of copper deposited on the given surface is so thin that its colour cannot be seen, dip the electrode for some time in a vessel with nitric acid; the presence of copper can then be detected by sodium diethyldithiocarbamate or rubeanic acid.

Copper can be separated similarly by electrolysis from solutions containing other metals (for example, iron, zinc or nickel).

Some data on the electrolytic separation of copper from solution are given in Table 8.

The separation of lead dioxide on a platinum anode. Prepare a solution of lead nitrate $\left(1\,\dfrac{m\gamma}{m\lambda}\,Pb\right)$. Electrolyse as described above with a voltage of 2·7 V and a current of 10^{-4} A.

A brown film of lead dioxide forms on the anode: this can be seen clearly under the microscope in reflected light. The solution remaining after electrolysis gives a negative reaction when tested for lead.

Some data on this process are given in Table 8.

TABLE 8. THE SEPARATION OF COPPER AND LEAD ON PLATINUM ELECTRODES

Electrolyte		Electrodes		Conditions of electrolysis			Products of electrolysis		Method of detection
Composition	Metal concentration, g/ml	Diameter, cm	Surface area, cm²	Voltage, V	Current, A	Time, min	Composition	Quantity g	
CuSO₄	8×10^{-3}	0·02	10^{-4}	2·2	10^{-4}	20	Cu	8×10^{-6}	By the characteristic colour of copper.
CuSO₄	1×10^{-3}	0·02	10^{-4}	2·2	10^{-4}	10	Cu	1×10^{-6}	
CuSO₄	1×10^{-3}	0·02	10^{-4}	2·2	10^{-4}	10	Cu	5×10^{-7}	By the characteristic colour of copper.
NiSO₄	1×10^{-3}								
FeSO₄	3×10^{-4}								
CuSO₄	1×10^{-3}	0·02	10^{-4}	2·2	10^{-4}	10	Cu	1×10^{-7}	By the characteristic colour of copper.
NiSO₄	1×10^{-3}								
FeSO₄	3×10^{-4}								
ZnSO₄	1×10^{-3}								
CuSO₄	5×10^{-5}	0·02	10^{-4}	2·2	10^{-4}	10	Cu	5×10^{-8}	By reaction with sodium diethyldithiocarbamate or rubeanic acid.
Pb(NO₃)₂	1×10^{-3}	0·02	10^{-4}	2·7	10^{-4}	10–15	PbO₂	5×10^{-7}	By the characteristic colour of the oxide.

Electrolyte Volume, ml column:
CuSO₄ 1×10^{-3};
CuSO₄ 1×10^{-3};
CuSO₄/NiSO₄/FeSO₄ $0·5 \times 10^{-3}$;
CuSO₄/NiSO₄/FeSO₄/ZnSO₄ $0·5 \times 10^{-3}$;
CuSO₄ 1×10^{-3};
Pb(NO₃)₂ $0·5 \times 10^{-3}$

6

Electrolysis on a Mercury Cathode

The method of electrolysis on a mercury cathode is widely used in analytical chemistry: it makes possible the separation of metals that cannot be isolated on platinum electrodes, for example, chromium, iron, molybdenum and so on.

Mercury occupies a special place as a cathode material. It requires different apparatus and a different technique. Further, the process of electrolysis on a mercury cathode is accompanied by vigorous evolution of gas bubbles and heating of the solution.

These last two features cause a number of complications in work on the ultramicroscale.

Apparatus

Electrolysis on a mercury cathode is done [44] in a capillary open at both ends. This is necessary because of the vigorous formation of gas during the process, which would force the solution out of an ordinary vessel or cone.

Prepare the mercury cathode by covering a platinum fork electrolytically (Fig. 22): the fork here serves as cathode (for which both wires must be connected to the same terminal). As electrolyte, use a solution of mercury nitrate (0·1 g in 0·05 ml nitric acid and 5·0 ml water). The anode is a third platinum wire, which is connected to the other terminal on the ebonite holder.

The mercury is deposited electrolytically on the fork in the microcone, the operation continuing until a drop of mercury is formed.

The electrodes thus obtained are those used for electrolysis on a mercury cathode (Fig. 23).

The current is supplied to the anode and cathode from an accumulator via a plug resistance box.

Procedure

On the holder in the moist chamber, place vessels for the necessary solutions and a capillary open at both ends. The capillary electrolyser must be of such diameter that the electrodes, when put into it, are a finite distance from the walls.

Place the chamber on the microscope stage. In the left manipulator fix the ebonite holder so that the anode is above the cathode; in the right fix the piston attachment with pipette.

Fill the vessels with the requisite solutions, then transfer measured volumes to the capillary. Place the solution at a distance of about a third of the length occupied by its volume from the end of the capillary facing the pipette. Turn the open side of the chamber to the left manipulator. Observing first with the naked eye, and then under the microscope, introduce the electrodes into the electrolyser capillary without letting them touch the solution. Connect up the current source and close the circuit

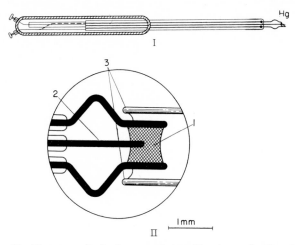

FIG. 23. Mercury cathode: I—general view; II—view under the microscope: 1—mercury cathode; 2—platinum anode; 3—capillary with solution.

by moving the capillary on to the electrodes until the latter reach the further meniscus of the solution. Observe the electrolytic process under the microscope. Determine the end of the process by the negative reaction with the relevant reagent; then withdraw the electrodes from the solution and disconnect the current source.

Once the metal is deposited on the mercury cathode, the mercury can be driven off. This is easily achieved by connecting the cathode into a circuit as a microheater. The metal remaining on the fork after the mercury has been driven off can be dissolved by immersion in a microcone with the appropriate solvent; the metal is then detected in the solution.

Examples of the Deposition of Metals on a Mercury Cathode

The separation of vanadium from copper and iron. Prepare solutions of copper and iron sulphate and a solution of ammonium vanadate in 2 N sulphuric acid.

The voltage used on the macroscale for electrolysis on a mercury cathode cannot be recommended for the electrolysis of small volumes, because, at such a voltage, the process is very violent and the solution is scattered as spray and evaporated in a very short time.

Separate vanadium from copper and iron at a voltage of $3\cdot8$–$3\cdot3$ V and a current of $3\cdot8$–$3\cdot3 \times 10^{-4}$ A, obtaining the necessary conditions by selecting the correct resistance in the plug box.

Electrolyse as described above in a capillary open at both ends.

Stop the process when the electrolyte gives a negative reaction with potassium ferro- and ferricyanide. Detect the presence of vanadium in the electrolyte remaining by reaction with cupferron.

The volumes of the solutions and the quantity by weight of the substances used in the electrolysis are given in Table 9.

The separation of vanadium from chromium. Prepare a solution of a chromate and a solution of ammonium vanadate in 2 N sulphuric acid.

Electrolyse as in the previous experiment, using a voltage of $3\cdot6$–$3\cdot4$ V and a current of $3\cdot6$–$3\cdot4 \times 10^{-4}$ A.

Stop the process when the solution gives a negative reaction for chromium with diphenylcarbazide.

The volumes and quantities of the substances used are given in Table 9.

SEPARATION ON ION-EXCHANGE RESINS

Ion-exchange methods find ever increasing application in inorganic analytical chemistry for the separation of very complex mixtures.* In comparison with other methods of separating elements (precipitation, extraction, distillation, electrolysis and so on) ion-exchange provides a procedure that is at once simpler and more versatile.

In ultramicroanalysis, separation by ion-exchange has the additional advantage (by comparison with precipitation, for example) that the element to be isolated can frequently be obtained in an extremely pure form without the introduction into the solution of a reagent which it is hard to remove subsequently. On the other hand, thanks to the small volumes of solution used in this type of work and the small amount of absorbing material needed ($0\cdot05$–$0\cdot1$ g), the time taken by the process is greatly reduced.

The technique of ion-exchange on the ultramicroscale does not

---

* See, for example, the symposium *Ion Exchange and Its Application* (Ionnyi obmen i yego primeneniye), Publishing House of the Acad. Sc. U.S.S.R., Moscow, 1959; O. SAMUELSON, *Ion Exchange in Analytical Chemistry* (Ionnyi obmen v analiticheskoi khimii), Foreign Literature Publ. House, Moscow, 1955.

TABLE 9. THE SEPARATION OF ELEMENTS BY ELECTROLYSIS ON A MERCURY CATHODE

Electrolyte			Conditions of electrolysis				Separated on cathode		Left in solution	
Composition	Metal concentration, g/ml	Volume, ml	Surface area of cathode, cm^2	Voltage, V	Current, A	Time, min	Element	Quantity, g	Element	Quantity, g
CuSO$_4$	1×10^{-3}	0.5×10^{-3}	2×10^{-3}	3.8–3.4	3.8–3.4 $\times 10^{-4}$	15	Cu	5×10^{-7}	—	—
FeSO$_4$	3×10^{-4}	0.5×10^{-3}					Fe	1.5×10^{-7}	—	—
CuSO$_4$	1×10^{-3}	0.3×10^{-3}	2×10^{-3}	3.8–3.4	3.8–3.4 $\times 10^{-4}$	15–20	Cu	3×10^{-7}		
FeSO$_4$	3×10^{-4}	0.5×10^{-3}					Fe	1.5×10^{-7}	V	1.5×10^{-7}
NH$_4$VO$_3$ (H$_2$SO$_4$)	2×10^{-4}	0.5×10^{-3}								
K$_2$Cr$_2$O$_7$	2×10^{-4}	0.5×10^{-3}	2×10^{-3}	3.6–3.4	3.6–3.4 $\times 10^{-4}$	15	Cr	1×10^{-7}	V	1×10^{-7}
NH$_4$VO$_3$ (H$_2$SO$_4$)	2×10^{-4}	0.5×10^{-3}								

differ in principle from conventional practice: the solution is passed in one direction through a layer of ion-exchange material. The scale of operation does, however, necessitate certain changes in apparatus and manipulation.

Apparatus

The apparatus used for the ion-exchange separation of small volumes of mixtures is a column consisting of a thin-walled capillary of 2–2·5 mm dia. and 3–4 cm length which opens out slightly towards the top. In the narrow part of the capillary a ridge is made, on which is fused in the flame of a microburner a sintered glass filter. Finally this end of the capillary is drawn out into a tip of 0·1 mm dia.

The filtrates are collected in ordinary microvessels of 1·5–2 mm dia., and the solution is introduced into the column by a micropipette with its tip bent at right angles.

The pressure required to force the solution out of the column is obtained from a gravity arrangement (see p. 115), which is connected to the column by a glass and rubber tube.

The apparatus described is set up as follows (Fig. 24). The column (1) is held in a clamp on a stand with a racking gear (2), the stand being fixed to a massive plate (3). The vessels are placed in a circle on a cylindrical Plexiglass holder (4), on which they are held by a rubber clamping ring. The holder can be rotated by a worm gear. The micropipette is fixed in the manipulator (5), which is also fixed to the plate.

Procedure for Separation by Ion-exchange

Fill the column with water by micropipette, and then with a micro-spatula introduce the necessary quantity (0·05–0·1 g) of prepared finely ground moist ion-exchange material, dipping the spatula into the water each time. (The microspatula is a flattened wire of about 0·2 mm dia.) With the column thus loaded, connect it to the gravity apparatus: force the water out of it two or three times until each time the meniscus reaches a level about 2 mm from the top of the ion-exchanger. This packs the layer of material closely. Then detach the column from the gravity apparatus, take the solution to be analysed from its vessel in the chamber with the micropipette and transfer it to the column. Again connect the column to the gravity arrangement, regulating the pressure to ensure the correct speed of flow of the solution. Set the column so that its tip touches the inside wall of one of the vessels by use of the racking gear, the vessel in its turn being brought under the column by rotation of the Plexiglass holder.

When the vessel is full, raise the column and at once bring up the next

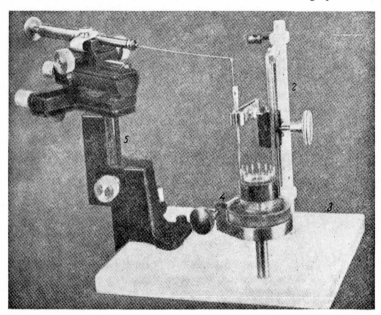

FIG. 24. Apparatus for separation by ion-exchange on the ultramicroscale.

vessel, and so on until the separation is completed with each fraction collected separately.

In each of the fractions obtained by one means or another (frontal analysis, analysis by washing, or displacement analysis) determine the components isolated from the mixture by the appropriate chemical method.

Examples of Separation by Ion-exchange

The Separation of Iron and Nickel

Fe^{3+} and Ni^{2+} can be separated by frontal analysis. Use is made of the ability of Ni^{2+} to form a complex with the nitrite ion.

To a solution containing $2 \frac{m\gamma}{m\lambda}$ Fe and $1 \frac{m\gamma}{m\lambda}$ Ni add solid sodium nitrite.
Pass the mixture obtained, which occupies 1–2 λ, through a column of KU-2 cationite, as described above. Fe^{3+} is absorbed, while nickel passes through the filter in the form $Ni(NO_2)_6^{4-}$. Replace the vessel containing $Ni(NO_2)_6^{4-}$ with a fresh vessel. Pass 2 N hydrochloric acid through the column and to wash out the Fe^{3+} as well.

The Separation of Chromium and Vanadium

Cr^{3+} and VO_2^+ can be separated for analysis by elution.

Pass 2–3 λ of an acid solution containing 1 γ chromium and 0·5 γ vanadium through a column of cationite: both components are absorbed. Wash the column with a 5 per cent ammonia solution to obtain vanadate in the filtrate and then, if necessary, extract the Cr^{3+} from the column with a 2 N hydrochloric acid solution.

SEPARATION BY EXTRACTION

The extraction method is widely used in analytical chemistry for separating elements, and also for increasing the sensitivity of reactions associated with the formation of coloured complexes.*

The extracting agents used are organic solvents,† which, as is well known, have the property of evaporating quickly thanks to their high vapour pressure or small latent heat of evaporation.

In extraction from small volumes with small quantities of organic solvents, their property of rapid evaporation begins to play an especially important part. Recourse must be had to a number of supplementary devices to prevent, to a greater or lesser degree, the rapid evaporation of the extracting agent. The methods of extraction described below can be used for work with volumes of the order of 10^{-3} to 10^{-5} ml on the microscope stage.

Apparatus

Small volumes of liquids can be extracted without the use of special apparatus. If a single treatment with solvent suffices, the extraction

* I. P. ALIMARIN and V. N. POLYANSKII, *Trudy Moscovskogo vechernego metallurgicheskogo instituta*, vyp. II, p. 187, Metallurgizdat, Moscow, 1957.

† C. MORRISON and H. FREISER, *Solvent Extraction in Analytical Chemistry.* New York, 1957.

is done in a capillary 0·5–1·0 mm in diameter and 2 cm long that has been sealed at one end [33].

Mixing in this case is accomplished by centrifugation.

If the extraction is to be repeated several times, it is more convenient to use a microcone. The microcone used (Fig. 25) differs somewhat from the normal type. The place where the extraction is done is the narrow part of this Y-shaped cone. The cone is made as follows.

FIG. 25. Microcone for extraction.

Take a capillary of about 1·5 mm dia. and draw it down in the flame of a microburner to a diameter of about 0·5 mm. Then, about 3–5 mm from the constriction draw the capillary so obtained into a rod, which serves as the foot of the microcone. Cut off the wide diameter part of the cone so that this part is about 2–3 mm long.

The contents of this cone are mixed by an electrovibrator, which consists of an ordinary electric bell with the dome removed. The distance between the pressure contact plate and the hammer is set so that the hammer vibrates almost too fast to be seen. A switch is mounted on the same board as the bell. The electrovibrator is connected to an alternating current source. If the switch is made and a capillary with the microcone brought up to the vibrating hammer, the vibrations will mix the contents of the microcone thoroughly.

Procedure

Place in the moist chamber a holder with the necessary vessels, including the extraction capillary or microcone. The latter is best placed in a capillary containing a drop of the substance that is to be used for the given extraction. Place the chamber on the microscope stage. In the jaws of the right manipulator fix the piston attachment with a micropipette.

Prepare the solution to be extracted in one of the cones. Then transfer this solution to the extraction vessel. When the microcone is used, the solution must occupy not more than half of the narrow part. Fill the pipette with the extraction agent from a cone with a bent stem and transfer it as quickly as possible to the capillary or extractor-microcone.

If a capillary is used, as soon as the extracting agent is added, take the capillary out of the holder, seal up the other end and mix the contents by centrifuging from one end to the other, turning the capillary round each time. Cut the capillary at the boundary between the two liquids.

If a microcone is used, force the solvent out of the pipette into the microcone, so that a layer of it ends up underneath a layer of the solution, even if at no great depth.

Introduce the extraction agent in drops, allowing the drop to travel some way in the solution before breaking off from the pipette tip; in this way the extraction is effected.

Then take the capillary with the extractor microcone out of the holder, seal up the open end of the capillary and transfer it to the electrovibrator so that the latter touches the capillary just at the point where the solution is in the microcone. After mixing, centrifuge the contents of the microcone in the same capillary. At this point the solution is divided into two layers, whose position relative to one another is determined by their specific gravity.

Next score the capillary and break open the end which the mouth of the microcone faces and return the capillary to the holder in the chamber.

Separate the layers by means of the pipette and transfer the organic extract to another microcone. If necessary, treat the aqueous layer with the organic solvent two, three or more times, and combine all the extracts.

To detect the element taken up into the organic solvent, use the characteristic colour, if possible; otherwise remove the solvent, making use of its rapid evaporation properties. Then dissolve the dry residue in a suitable solvent and carry out the necessary reactions in an aqueous solution.

Finally, make the necessary determinations with the elements left in the aqueous solution after extraction.

We give one example of this method.

The Extraction of Vanadium Cupferronate

Prepare a solution of ammonium vanadate $\left(0{\cdot}5\dfrac{m\gamma}{m\lambda}\,V\right)$ sulphuric acid and a 6 per cent solution of cupferron.

Assemble the piston attachment with a pipette and fix in the right manipulator. In the holder in the chamber place two microvessels and an extractor microcone in a capillary containing a drop of chloroform.

Fill the vessels with the prepared solution. Transfer 10 mλ of the vanadium solution by pipette to the microcone, add approximately twice the volume of water, then add the necessary amount of the cupferron solution. A precipitate, vanadium cupferronate, is formed. Without separating the solution from the precipitate, add chloroform to the cone by pipette. Draw the chloroform up into the pipette from a cone with a bent stem: after removing the cone, make one or two turns of the screw in the same direction, because the chloroform will try to run out of the pipette.

After adding the chloroform seal the capillary, mix by electrovibration and centrifuge. Separate the layers with a pipette. Observe the colour of vanadium cupferronate solution in chloroform using a coloriscopic capillary (see p. 36).

SEPARATION BY SUBLIMATION AND DISTILLATION

For the separation of certain elements sublimation methods are used and also distillation in the form of volatile complexes.

The general principles of sublimation and distillation of small quantities and volumes follow conventional practice: the desired separation is achieved by the heating of the solution from which one or other component is to be driven off, and by the collection of the distillate in a cooled receiver.

Apparatus [33]

Small quantities of a substance or volume of a liquid can be sublimed or distilled without the use of special apparatus. All that is needed is a microcone about 1 cm long and one of like diameter to serve as the receiver: the microcone from which the substance is to be driven off should fit snugly into the receiver. The necessary heating for sublimation or distillation is produced by an electric microheater.

Procedure

Place in the holder in a dry chamber the necessary vessels: these will include a receiver cone of such diameter that the cone from which the substance is to be driven off, fits snugly into it.

If cooling is needed to condense the distillate in the receiver, the latter must be placed in a capillary with a piece of dry ice.

Place the chamber with the vessels on the microscope stage. In the jaws of the right manipulator fix the piston attachment with a pipette (in the case of distillation out of a solution) or a glass piston device (see p. 89) for transferring a dry substance. In the left manipulator fix a microheater.

Into the cone that fits tightly into the receiver place the solution (or solid substance) from which distillation is to be made. Then remove the cone containing the solution from the holder with tweezers and take it by the stem in the left hand.

Take the receiver out of the holder with the tweezers and, holding it in a horizontal position, place the cone with the solution into it and return it to the holder. Turn the open side of the chamber towards the microheater and bring the latter up to the cone with the solution on the level of the receiver (Fig. 26). Switch on the current and slowly increase the voltage, watching continuously under the microscope the while. The field of view of the microscope is not generally large enough to get the whole distillation apparatus in focus at one time; therefore focus the microscope

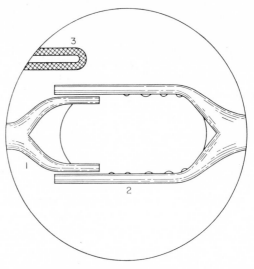

FIG. 26. Distillation (view under the microscope): 1—microvessel with the initial solution; 2—receiver microvessel; 3—heater.

on the apex of the cone with the solution and watch the evaporation of this solution to the necessary volume. The movement of the meniscus towards the apex of the cone should be slow. Regulate the speed of this movement by changing the position of the microheater in relation to the cones, or by changing the voltage passed to the microheater.

Then withdraw the microheater from the chamber and bring the receiver cone into the field of view: drops of solution (or crystals of a solid substance) are now visible on the walls.

Repeat the distillation as often as necessary.

When the distillation is complete, remove the lid of the chamber, take the cone containing the residue of solution (or solid) out of the receiver with tweezers and place it beside the other in the holder. Then place the receiver in a capillary for centrifuging. Centrifugation collects the drops of solution off the walls of the receiver into its apex. Next score the receiver vessel and break off the end with tweezers, reducing it to the normal length of a cone (4–5 mm); return the receiver to the holder in the chamber.

This cone can now be used to detect the presence of the distilled element by the appropriate reagent.

Examples of Sublimation and Distillation

The Sublimation of Iodine

Grind crystals of iodine to a fine powder. Place a cone and receiver of appropriate diameters in a dry chamber.

With the aid of the glass piston device transfer a suitable amount of iodine to the cone.

Place the cone in the receiver in such a position that the latter is turned stem down to avoid spilling powder from it. Then bring the cones carefully to the horizontal position, place them on the holder in the chamber with the stem of the receiver in the opening of the holder.

Distil as described above, watching through the microscope the while. On conclusion of the distillation observe on the walls of the receiver the characteristic crystals of iodine.

The Sublimation of Mercury

Mix a small quantity of mercury oxide and iron powder in a small mortar. Heat the mixture so obtained as described above: as a result droplets of metallic mercury appear on the walls of the receiver. Then place the receiver in a centrifuge and collect the droplets off the walls into the apex. In the cone from which the mercury has been driven off there remains iron powder, which can be distinguished from the original mixture by its darker colour.

The Separation of Arsenic by the Distillation of its Chloride [33]

Prepare hydrochloric acid solutions of antimony (III) chloride and potassium arsenate, a 0·5 M solution of nitric acid, a 3 M solution of phosphoric acid and a 9 M solution of hydrobromic acid.

Concentrated solutions of hydrochloric and nitric acid and solid potassium bromate are also required.

In the holder in the moist chamber place four vessels, two cones and two measuring capillaries. In addition, a dry chamber is required containing three vessels, one cone and a receiver cone for the distillation.

Place the moist chamber on the microscope stage. In the jaws of the right manipulator clamp the piston attachment with a pipette. Fill one of the vessels in the moist chamber with distilled water, another with the 0·5 M solution of nitric acid, a third with the solution of arsenic salt and the fourth with the antimony salt solution.

The measuring capillaries are used to measure definite volumes of the solutions of arsenic and antimony salts.

Using the pipette and measuring with the measuring capillaries, transfer to one of the cones about 7 mλ of the solution of antimony (50 mγ of antimony) and about 3 mλ of arsenic solution (25 mγ of arsenic). Dilute the solution to 100 mλ with distilled water and mix with the pipette. Treat with hydrogen sulphide, then heat in a sealed capillary in a water bath for one minute. Leave to stand at room temperature for about 30 min. Then centrifuge and measure the volume of sulphides obtained. Separate the supernatant solution and discard. Transfer the cone with the precipitate to the dry chamber and place the latter on the microscope stage. Fill one of the vessels in it with concentrated hydrochloric acid, the second with the 9 M solution of hydrobromic acid and the third with the 3 M solution of phosphoric acid.

Treat the precipitate in the cone transferred from the moist chamber with 30 ml of concentrated hydrochloric acid while heating in a water bath in a sealed capillary. Mix the contents of the cone with an electro-vibrator. Then return the cone to the dry chamber and add small amounts of solid potassium bromate until only sulphur remains in the cone. Centrifuge the contents of the cone and return it to the dry chamber. Wash the sulphur residue with 40 mλ of concentrated hydrochloric acid and add the washing solution to the main solution. Treat this solution with 10 mλ of 9 M hydrobromic acid and 20 mλ of 3 M phosphoric acid to reduce the antimony and arsenic oxidized in solution.

Seal the cone in a capillary and place it in a water bath at 80–90°. Then cool the capillary with the cone, centrifuge, remove the cone from the capillary and put it into the receiver cone. Distil as described above, repeating it twice; first distil down to a volume of about 15 mλ, then treat the residue with 10 mλ of concentrated hydrochloric acid and distil again to a volume of 10 mλ. Owing to its high volatility, the arsenic is driven off into the distillate. Transfer the cone with the residue from the distillation to the holder in the moist chamber. Centrifuge the contents of the receiver, thus collecting the distillate in the apex. Shorten the receiver and return it to the dry chamber. Then transfer the distillate with a pipette into an ordinary cone. Dilute the residue from the distillation with 50 mλ of distilled water and treat with hydrogen sulphide. Collect the precipitate in the apex of the cone by centrifugation and measure the volume. The orange colour of antimony sulphide is clearly distinguishable in reflected light. Dilute the distillate in the cone in the moist chamber with water to 100 mλ. Treat the solution so obtained with 40 mλ of concentrated hydrochloric acid and saturate with hydrogen sulphide; heat in a water bath and mix by electrovibration. Collect the precipitate in the apex of the cone by centrifugation. Place the cone in the moist chamber and estimate the volume of precipitate. The yellow colour of the arsenic sulphide is clearly seen in reflected light.

The volumes of the two precipitates so obtained are approximately in the following ratio to one another:

$$v_{As_2S_3} : v_{Sb_2S_3} : (v_{As_2S_3} + v_{Sb_2S_3}) = 1:2:3$$

CHAPTER V

THE QUALITATIVE ANALYSIS OF VARIOUS SAMPLES

THE PREPARATION OF THE SAMPLE FOR ANALYSIS

Small Samples

Various methods of preparation for analysis are used depending on the sample to be investigated.

1. *Small volumes of liquids.* Here the preparation for analysis consists simply of the exact measurement of the initial solution, and subsequent careful taking of aliquots with precise determination of the volume remaining each time. This last is necessary because of the high speed of evaporation from small volumes, which must be decreased by the use of special methods for preserving the solutions. Benedetti-Pichler [33] recommends that small volumes of solutions should be kept by sealing the microvessel into a capillary containing a drop of the liquid used as the solvent in the solution to be preserved. El-Badry and Wilson [39] use for this purpose a round plastic block with holes drilled for the vessels: in the central hole they put moist cotton wool (Fig. 27). The block is covered with a Petri or crystallizing dish. It is also convenient to keep the solutions directly in the moist chamber, closing the open side with cotton wool and placing the chamber into a Petri dish.

2. *Deposits and films.* Here the substance to be analysed is best removed mechanically without disturbing the background material. This is conveniently done with the fused end of a pipette tip or platinum wire (even if only a single platinum electrode is used for this purpose). The layer of the substance is loosened (if necessary) while observed under the microscope; it is then transferred to a microvessel. This last operation is effected by a method described by Benedetti-Pichler [33] for adding solid reagents to a solution.

79

As a rule, it is best to transfer the substance to be analysed to a microvessel with distilled water, and then to collect it in the apex of the vessel by centrifugation. If the water is going to interfere with the subsequent analytical procedure, it can be driven off and the sample carefully dried with a microheater.

3. *Inclusions in a metal or alloy.* Inclusions can very frequently be isolated by drilling. Various drills or sharpened steel needles are used for this, the drilling being done under a microscope. Various types of suitable apparatus have been described. A very convenient

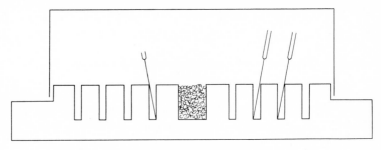

FIG. 27. Block for preserving small volumes of solutions.

construction is that described by Rusanov [73]. An ordinary dentist's drill is fitted with a holder for steel needles that is precisely centred. This drill is inserted in the left side of a binocular microscope, from which the objective and the eyepiece tube have been removed. The object from which the inclusion is to be drilled is fixed on the stage with plasticine. The needle is set while stationary on the centre of the inclusion, the microscope is focused and the drill rotated and simultaneously lowered by the microscope racking gear. In this way inclusions of up to 0·2 mm dia. can be drilled out.

Steel needles are suitable for drilling materials not harder than quartz. For harder materials a finely sharpened tungsten-cobalt carbide tip can be used.

Kalyuzhnyi [74] proposes an apparatus of somewhat different construction, but working on the same principle. Particularly deserving of attention is the fact that the sample is placed on a metal plate whose edges rest on a rubber cushion. This affords some measure of protection against accidental damage to the drill.

For drilling out smaller and at the same time superficial inclusions, the device suggested by Krushchov and Berkovich [75, 76] should be used. This device is a modification of the PMT-2 or PMT-3 instruments for testing microhardness. The essentially new detail is a special attachment fitted with a diamond drill.

FIG. 28. General view of the PMT-2 instrument with the drill for taking filings.

In general, the PMT-2 instrument (Fig. 28) is a vertical bench microscope of the metal microscope type, fitted with a coordinate stage which can be rotated.

The drilling attachment to the PMT-3 consists of two bushes (1) and (2) (Fig. 29): bush (1) is screwed on to the projecting threaded part of the hollow stock of the loading mechanism (3), while bush (2) fits in the place of the diamond tip. The shaft of the drill (4) is

7

seated in the apertures of these two bushes. To the upper part of the shaft is fixed the holder (5) of the drill with four projections (6). The holder (5) is fixed on the drill beam at such a height that a gap of 0·1–0·2 mm forms between the parts (1) and (5) during drilling. The drill is rotated clockwise by hand by means of a peg which touches the projections (6) successively. The weights (7) are put on

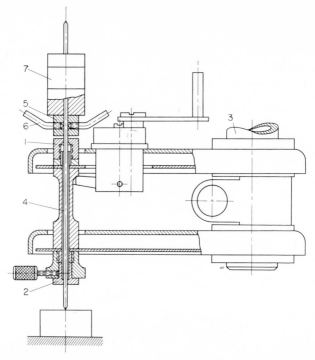

FIG. 29. Diagram of the drilling attachment to the PMT-2 instrument.

the holder (5) to provide the cutting power. Three different weights, depending on the hardness of the sample, suffice. In both types, the drill is a trihedral pyramid with an angle of 142° at the apex between one side and the opposite rib. The trihedral drill is stable at the beginning of the drilling and can be sharpened very finely in preparation. A diamond drill is used for drilling hard samples. In preparing and setting such a drill it is essential to ensure that the axis of the drill shaft is coaxial with the axis of the sharpening of the trihedral pyramid. The final lapping of one of the sides of the pyramid, which consists in the precise juxtaposition of both axes of the pyramid and the drill shaft, is done on the instrument by making test impressions in one place while rotating the pyramid each time through 120°. If the apex of the pyramid lies on the axis of the drill shaft, then all three impressions coincide completely. Any eccentricity is corrected by the shifting (displacement) of one or two sides of the drill.

The technique of using the drill is as follows.

Place the sample on the microscope stage, which must be turned right down on to its support. While viewing the surface of the sample through the microscope and moving the stage by the two screws of the coordinate transmission, find the spot for taking the test and make it coincide with the intersections of the threads of the screw eyepiece micrometer. Then turn the stage to the other extreme position up to the support, so that the drill shaft axis now coincides with the chosen point. Lower the drill till it touches the sample and set it rotating by means of the hand drive: it is now possible to drill out at the chosen spot. Return the stage with the sample to the initial position and measure the diameter of the drilled depression by means of the screw eyepiece micrometer: in this way it is possible to estimate the depth of the hole and the volume drilled out, and also to check the precision with which the test has been taken from the chosen spot. For a diameter of 50 μ, the volume of metal drilled out is 3750×10^{-9} mm^3; in the case of iron this means approximately 3×10^{-8} g.

It should be noted that the surface of the sample must be polished. During the drilling process shavings are scattered over the surface around the hole, forming a fairly solid ring. These shavings may then be transferred to a micro-vessel using the normal method involving a thin glass or platinum tip; it is necessary to put the sample with the drillings on the microscope stage.

The Concentrating of Impurities

If the major component of some very pure material (for example, semi-conducting germanium, silicon and so on) is removed, then ultramicroanalytical techniques make it possible to determine in the residue the micro-impurities in the main substance, provided that they are first concentrated in a small volume. The reagents used to remove the major component must also have the property of being completely expelled from the solution on further concentration of the impurities. Concentration is most simply achieved by evaporation, which, in a given case, can be used to produce a gradual reduction in the volume of solution, vessels of ever smaller dimensions being used. Here it is better to do repeated evaporations in the same vessels rather than to use a great number. Best of all for evaporation is a vessel of fluorinated plastic, because this material is very

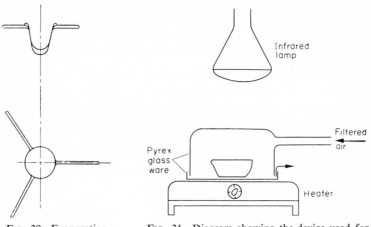

FIG. 30. Evaporating cup.

FIG. 31. Diagram showing the device used for protecting the system from contamination out of the air during evaporation.

stable against the action of various reagents, even *aqua regia*, at temperatures of 300–400°. Thanks to this, the walls do not provide a source of contamination for the solution to be evaporated.

In the last stage (before the microscope), when violent reagents can no longer be used, it is convenient to use quartz cups of a special shape (Fig. 30), with a volume of 0·1–0·05 ml. The evaporation should be done carefully and the vapours given off removed by a stream of air or some inert gas, transmitted by a tube with its tip drawn out into a capillary, the tube being fixed above the cup containing the solution. Care should also be taken during evaporation to avoid dust contamination (Fig. 31).

The solution should be transferred from one vessel to another by pipette and not by simple pouring, because this involves inevitable losses.

After the solution in the smallest cup has been evaporated down to about half its volume, one of the stems is broken off the cup, which is then placed on the remaining two stems in an inclined position under the microscope on the lid of the dry chamber; in the chamber there is a microvessel for further concentration. The solution is gradually transferred to this vessel by pipette and evaporated down to its final volume with an electric microheater.

The reagents used directly for determining the impurities need not be especially pure, because the conditions of use are analogous to those of normal macroanalysis.

On the other hand, the reagents used in preparing the sample for ultramicroanalysis (solution of the sample and removal of the basic component) must be very pure, because in this case impurities in the reagents will be concentrated together with the impurities in the sample under investigation. In this connexion, the problem of purifying and preserving the reagents takes on great significance. The information given below on the purification of the more commonly used reagents has been taken from Yoe and Koch's book [77].

The Purification and Preservation of Reagents

Water should be prepared by ion exchange and subsequent distillation in quartz apparatus. In the ion-exchange column metal ions are removed from the water, while the subsequent distillation frees the water from unionized substances and also nitrogen compounds, a small amount of which is leached out of the resin. The electrical conductivity of such water is $3 \times 10^{-7}\ \Omega^{-1}$, as compared with a value of $1 \cdot 7 \times 10^{-6}\ \Omega^{-1}$ for thrice distilled water. The ion content of such water as compared with normal distilled water is shown in Fig. 32 for a number of ions.

Hydrochloric acid can be obtained in its purest form by the dissolution of non-aqueous hydrogen chloride in pure water. The gas is purified by being passed through concentrated sulphuric acid, then through a layer of glass wool (Pyrex glass), after which it passes through a layer of distilled water saturated with hydrogen chloride, finally being dissolved in water that has been purified by the method described above. In this way, acid about 12 M can be obtained. The metallic impurities in such acid are present in practically the same quantities as in the water used to dissolve the gas.

Nitric acid is purified by repeated distillation of an azeotropic compound (65 per cent nitric acid, 35 per cent water) in a quartz

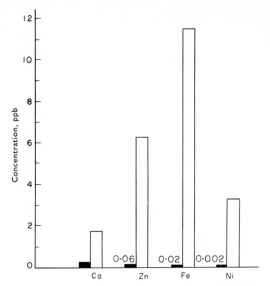

FIG. 32. Quantity of ions of several metals found in distilled water: []—simple distilled water; ▮—water after ion exchange.

apparatus. The product obtained is not sufficiently pure; however, no other method of purifying nitric acid is known to date.

Sulphuric acid can be obtained in a very pure form by distillation in a quartz apparatus.

Ammonia is obtained very pure by saturating water with gaseous ammonia, like hydrochloric acid.

The purified reagents may be contaminated during storage by the material of the vessel, or by desorption from the walls of the vessel of ions adsorbed on to them earlier. The best vessels for keeping pure reagents are made of polyethylene, because this material is itself very pure and has practically no sorptive properties.

THE DISSOLUTION OF MICROSAMPLES OF A SUBSTANCE

Dissolution in Acids

If a substance is easily dissolved in any of the voltatile acids, it is very convenient to dissolve it gradually, using the acid as a gaseous reagent.

Distilled water is added to a cone containing the substance to be investigated. The cone is then placed in a bent capillary and the latter is connected to the apparatus for obtaining gaseous reagents. The water is gradually saturated with the vapour of the acid and the substance slowly dissolved.

In general, the acid is added directly to the cone with the sample. The acid should be added little by little with constant mixing with the pipette tip, so that the violent gas formation that takes place should not spray the solution out of the cone. The dissolution process should be observed under the microscope; also the solution should from time to time be drawn up into the pipette and then returned to the cone, this being an effective way of helping the removal of the gas formed. During the process the tip of the pipette should always be in the solution. If the dissolution in the cold stops, the contents of the cone should be heated with a microheater; in this case, the cone often has to be put in an exhaust chamber (see on the next page).

Decomposition by Means of Acid and Alkaline Fluxes

To dissolve solids insoluble in water and acids, the method of fusion with a flux is used.

As with all other operations under the microscope, a special procedure must be followed.

Apparatus

The fusion of a substance with a flux of low fusing point can be done in an ordinary glass or quartz microcone, whose apex must be as round as possible.

If the fusion is accompanied by the evolution of corrosive gases, the cone must be placed under the microscope in a holder inside a special chamber, which is like a fume box. This exhaust chamber (Fig. 33) is a glass tube with a flat bottom, flat back wall and a nozzle in one side. The chamber is connected to a water pump by this nozzle: in this way the gases evolved during fusion, which might

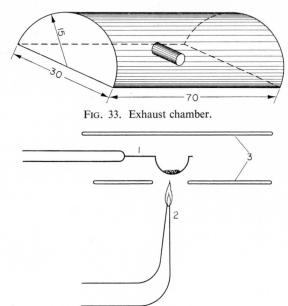

FIG. 33. Exhaust chamber.

FIG. 34. Fusion in a platinum cup: 1—platinum cup; 2—microburner; 3—chamber.

otherwise damage the metal parts of the microscope and manipulators, are removed.

Heat the compound to be fused with a microheater, its construction must be slightly different from that described above inasmuch as higher temperatures are required. Direct heating is done with a platinum wire, pressed into conducting copper leads.

Reinforce the pressed connexion with silver solder, dissolve a crystal of silver nitrate at the spot and heat in a microflame until the silver is reduced. Then pass the copper leads separately through porcelain tubes right up to the contacts, so that no copper shows outside the tubes (on reheating, they are rapidly oxidized in air). Pass both tubes together into a porcelain tube about 5 mm in diameter. The first tube should fit snugly into this tube; there should be only 5–10 mm showing at the front. Take the copper leads out of the other end of the tube to connect to the electrical circuit described earlier.

The fusion of a substance with a high melting point flux is done in a platinum cup 1–3 mm in diameter and 1–2 mm deep (Fig. 34, 1).

First press the copper leads in the handle of the cup, solder the contact with silver, cover the leads with capillaries and then insert the whole in a porcelain tube. Take the ends of the leads out of the tube to connect up to the electrical circuit. In this case, heating by electric current is used only for drying the flux. The actual fusion is done in a microflame, the microburner (2) being fixed under the microscope stage.

The fusion over the burner is done in the chamber (3), which has a glass bottom with an aperture for the admission of the burner; the lid is made of heat-resistant glass. A cuvette with plane parallel sides to protect the microscope objective from the heat is placed on the lid.

Solids are transferred to the fusion cone or the platinum cup by means of a glass piston device, which is made as follows.

Take a glass tube about 5–7 mm in diameter. At a distance of 7–8 cm from one end draw the tube out into a capillary 0·5–1 mm in diameter and 7–8 cm in length in the flame of a bunsen burner. Then draw the tip of this capillary out in a microflame to a diameter of 0·1–0·2 mm, leaving it 2–4 mm long. Then, again in the flame of an ordinary burner, draw out a glass rod into a thread at a distance of 9–10 cm from one end. The rod must be of such diameter that it fits freely, but snugly, into the glass tube selected. The thread, 7·5–8·5 cm long, must be 0·05–0·15 mm in diameter at a point about 1 cm from the tip. At the end opposite the thread, melt the rod into a pestle. Smear a layer of vacuum grease on to it and fit it into the glass tube with its end drawn out into a capillary. In this form the glass device is ready for use.

The Fusing Operation

In a microcone. Place the fusion cone in a holder in the glass exhaust chamber. Place the chamber on the microscope stage. Fix in the right manipulator the glass piston device, in the left a microheater. Into a cone with a bent stem (see p. 25) transfer the flux with a small glass spatula and lightly pack it down. Then bring the cone up to the drawn out tip of the capillary of the piston device. The little piston thread should not be in the tip at this stage. Use the manipulator to introduce the tip of the capillary into the layer of the substance. Manipulate the capillary up to the fusion cone whilst observing under the microscope and also with the naked eye. Move the piston forward, thus forcing the flux out of the capillary tip into the cone. Withdraw the piston device from the chamber and draw the piston back a little. Transfer a grain of the substance to be fused, using the method for transferring solid reagents; here use as a glass needle the piston of the glass device taken out of the capillary tip. Then again add flux. Withdraw the capillary of the piston device from the chamber. Turn the open side of the chamber towards the heater. Turn on the water pump and bring the heater up to the cone in the chamber.

Gradually reduce the resistance and heat the tip of the heater to red heat. Watch the fusion under the microscope. When the operation is concluded, shut off the water pump, remove the exhaust chamber from the stage, take the holder with the cone out of it and put it into a moist chamber. In the same holder place the vessels needed for further work.

Then fix the chamber on the microscope stage. Replace the glass piston device in the right manipulator by the piston attachment with a pipette. Dissolve the fused mass in the microcone with the relevant solvent and then work further with this solution.

In a platinum cup. On the stage place a dry chamber, whose bottom is made of glass with an aperture about 5 mm in diameter left in the middle. The chamber must be covered with a lid of heat-resistant glass, while the ends must be left open. Fix the platinum cup in the jaws of the left manipulator and introduce it into the chamber, positioning it over the hole in the bottom. Fix the glass piston device in the right manipulator. Transfer a grain of the substance to the cup. Fill the tip of the capillary of the piston device as described above and introduce it into the chamber, observing first with the naked eye and then under the microscope. Focus the microscope so that the upper surface of the cup is clearly to be seen. Lower the manipulator holding the glass piston device until a distinct image of the tip of the capillary appears; the capillary must be so positioned that its tip reaches about a third of the diameter of the cup. Then bring the bottom of the cup into focus. Slowly move the piston into the tip of the capillary, so forcing its contents out into the cup. Then raise it somewhat with the manipulator and withdraw it from the chamber. Connect the cup to an electric circuit and watch the drying of the material in it under the microscope. Then place a cuvette on the lid of the chamber and carefully bring up under the cup the microburner with a flame not more than 2 mm high.

Watch the fusion under the microscope. When this operation is completed, remove the heater and replace the glass piston device in the right manipulator by the piston attachment with a pipette, the tip of which is bent at right angles. Use this pipette to introduce the necessary solvent into the cup.

If a certain amount of heating is needed for the leaching, this is effected electrically. The same pipette is used to withdraw the solution so obtained from the cup.

Withdraw the cup from the chamber by means of the manipulator. Remove the chamber and replace it by a moist chamber containing the necessary vessels. In this case the vessel holder is turned through 90° to its normal position. Loosen the jaws of the right manipulator and turn the piston attachment in it so that the bent tip of the pipette lies horizontal. Transfer the solution in the pipette to one of the vessels. The solution is then ready for analysis.

Examples of the Fusing Operation

The fusion of titanium dioxide and niobium pentoxide with potassium pyrosulphate. Place in the exhaust chamber two cones of 0·5–1 mm dia. and transfer the chamber to the microscope stage. Fix the glass piston device in the right manipulator and a microheater in the left.

Fuse the titanium dioxide in one of the cones and the niobium pentoxide in the other, using potassium pyrosulphate as flux and placing the heater between the cones. Fuse for 5–10 min.

Treat the fused niobium pentoxide with a 10 per cent solution of tartaric acid, and the titanium dioxide with a dilute (1:15) solution of sulphuric acid. Continue the analysis with these solutions.

The fusion of vanadium pentoxide with sodium carbonate. Fix the platinum cup in the left manipulator. Place a chamber with a lid of heat-resisting glass on the stage. In the jaws of the right manipulator fix the glass piston device.

Fill the cup with the materials and fuse as described above. Leach the fused mass of vanadium pentoxide with water, transfer the solution obtained to a vessel in the moist chamber, treat this solution with 8-hydroxyquinoline and observe the formation of a dark precipitate.

This method may be used to separate vanadium from, for example, titanium, iron and other elements.

EXAMPLES OF THE ANALYSIS OF ALLOYS AND METALS

The Analysis of Ferrochrome

Reagents: A solution of sulphuric acid (1:1), solutions of potassium ferrocyanide and diphenylcarbazide, concentrated nitric acid and solid potassium bromate.

In the holder in a dry exhaust chamber place three vessels and three cones. Place the chamber on the microscope stage. Fix the piston attachment with a pipette in the right manipulator.

Turn on the water pump. Fill one vessel with distilled water, another with sulphuric and the third with nitric acid.

With the pipette transfer to one of the cones about 10 mλ of distilled water. Take the piston attachment and pipette out of the right manipulator and fix the glass piston device in its place. Bring the tip of the capillary of this last close up to the cone containing distilled water, and carefully move the piston-thread with bits of the alloy on it towards the aperture in the capillary tip. Dip the piston with the alloy into the water in the cone. Then draw the piston device back with the manipulator, leaving the alloy in the water.

The alloy particles lie on the surface of the meniscus, so they must be collected in the apex of the cone by centrifugation.

Again fix the piston attachment and pipette into the right manipulator. Return the cone to the holder in the chamber and add with the pipette 10–15 mλ of sulphuric acid, mixing thoroughly. After a time dissolution in the cold stops. Fix a microheater in the left manipulator, turn the open side of the chamber towards it and heat the solution in the cone. When almost all of the alloy has been dissolved, add 5–10 mλ of nitric acid to the cone and heat till the nitric oxides have been removed. Dilute with water to 50–70 mλ. Separate the undissolved residue by centrifugation. Transfer the solution to another cone. Remove the cone used for the dissolution and the citric acid vessel and place in the holder a new vessel for the potassium ferrocyanide solution. Then place the holder in an ordinary chamber. Replace the piston attachment in the right manipulator by a holder with a glass needle. On the lid of the chamber place a cover slip carrying potassium bromate ground to a fine powder. Add this to the solution in the cone with the glass needle. The green colour of the solution turns yellow owing to the chromium (III) ion being oxidized to the chromium (VI).

Remove the holder with the needle and again replace the piston attachment and pipette in the manipulator.

Precipitate hydrous iron (III) oxide from the solution with gaseous ammonia. Separate the solution from the precipitate and transfer it to another cone. Neutralize the solution and acidify it with the (1:1) sulphuric acid. Detect the presence of chromium by its reaction with diphenylcarbazide. Dissolve the hydrous iron (III) oxide precipitate in sulphuric acid and observe the formation of a blue precipitate when the potassium ferrocyanide solution is added.

The Analysis of Ferrovanadium

Reagents: Solutions of sulphuric acid (1:1), nitric acid (1:1), caustic soda, potassium thiocyanate 1·5 M, 8-hydroxyquinoline and acetic acid.

In a dry exhaust chamber in a holder place three vessels and two cones.

Place the chamber on the microscope stage. Fix the piston attachment with pipette in the right manipulator.

Fill one vessel with distilled water, a second with sulphuric acid and the third with nitric acid.

Dissolve in one of the cones as described above in the analysis of ferrochrome. Evaporate until there is abundant evolution of fumes of sulphuric acid and then dilute with water to 50–70 mλ.

Transfer the holder with the vessels to a normal chamber and place in it four clean vessels. Fill these vessels with the caustic soda, potassium thiocyanate, 8-hydroxyquinoline and acetic acid solutions.

The solution of ferrovanadium is coloured blue by vanadium (IV). Oxidize it with potassium bromate, as described in the previous experiment. Out of the solution so obtained precipitate the hydrous iron oxide with caustic soda, separate the solution from the precipitate and transfer it to another cone. Add 8-hydroxyquinoline and observe the formation of a dark precipitate.

Dissolve the precipitate of hydrous iron oxide in nitric acid and observe that the solution takes on a red colour on the addition of the thiocyanate solution.

The Analysis of Brass

Reagents: Solutions of sulphuric acid (0·2 N), caustic soda, potassium ferrocyanide and concentrated nitric acid.

In the holder in a normal chamber, place three vessels and three cones. Place the chamber on the microscope stage. In the jaws of the right manipulator fix a metal holder with a glass needle covered with a thin film of glycerine.

On the roof of the chamber place on a glass rod a cover slip [33] carrying a flake of brass weighing about 10 γ. Transfer this flake with a glass needle to one of the cones, in which there should be a small quantity of water. Then evaporate off the water with a microheater. Place the holder with the vessels in an exhaust chamber, and transfer the latter to the stage in place of the ordinary chamber. Turn on the water pump. Now fix the piston attachment and pipette into the right manipulator in place of the holder with the needle.

Fill the vessels with distilled water, concentrated nitric acid and dilute sulphuric acid respectively.

Transfer about 70 mλ of concentrated nitric acid to the cone containing the flake of brass. Control the dissolution, which begins at once, by mixing the solution with the pipette. Evaporate till the nitric oxides are driven off, and then to dryness, by heating the solution with a microheater fixed in the left manipulator. During this operation the open side of the chamber must be turned towards the heater.

Transfer the holder with the vessels to an ordinary chamber, remove the nitric acid vessel and replace it by a microcone for electrolysis, and also a clean vessel to be filled with the potassium ferrocyanide solution.

Dissolve the dry residue in dilute sulphuric acid, on which part of the iron remains in the form of the hydrous oxide. Separate the solution from the precipitate by centrifugation and transfer it to the electrolysis-microcone, and dilute it to a volume of about 3 λ.

Electrolyse with fork electrodes (see p. 62 and Fig. 22) at a voltage of 2·2 V and a current of 10^{-4} A. The cathode becomes covered with a layer of copper, the red colour of which can easily be seen when examined in reflected light.

After electrolysis, transfer part of the solution (30–40 mλ) to a clean cone and treat with an excess of alkali, to obtain a precipitate of hydrous iron (III) oxide. Separate the solution from the precipitate and transfer it to another cone. Treat the precipitate again with alkali and combine this solution with that in the cone. Neutralize the solution and acidify with sulphuric acid (1:1). Now add to the solution in the cone the solution of potassium ferrocyanide, and observe in reflected light the formation of the white precipitate of the zinc salt.

The Analysis of Vanadinite

Reagents: Solutions of sulphuric acid, caustic soda, cupferron, potassium iodide and concentrated hydrochloric acid.

In the holder in the exhaust chamber place six vessels and four cones. Place the chamber on the microscope stage, turn on the water pump. In the jaws of the right manipulator fix the piston attachment with pipette, in the left a microheater. Fill the six vessels with the respective solutions.

Replace the pipette in the right manipulator by the glass piston device and use it to place in one of the cones a few flakes of vanadinite. Again fix the piston attachment in the right manipulator, and use it to transfer to the cone containing the vanadinite about 50 mλ of concentrated hydrochloric acid. Control the dissolution by mixing with the pipette as described above.

Dissolution in the cold ceases after 5–10 minutes; thereupon dilute the solution with about twice the quantity of distilled water. The characteristic crystals of lead chloride come down. Centrifuge, separate the solution from the precipitate and transfer it to another cone. Add distilled water to the precipitate and heat, turning the open side of the chamber to the heater, which is fixed in the left manipulator. After dissolving the precipitate add to the solution obtained the potassium iodide solution and observe in reflected light the formation of brilliant yellow crystals of lead iodide.

From the solution separated from the lead chloride precipitate, precipitate the hydrous iron (III) oxide with alkali. Separate the solution from the precipitate and transfer it to a clean cone. Neutralize it and acidify with dilute sulphuric acid; add cupferron solution and observe the formation of the brown precipitate, vanadium cupferronate, which can also be extracted with chloroform.

TABLE 10. THE SENSITIVITY OF VARIOUS METHODS OF QUALITATIVE ULTRAMICROANALYSIS

Method of detection or separation		Element	Compound	Mass of element, g	Volume of solution, ml
Precipitation		Silver	Silver chloride	1×10^{-7}	10^{-5}
		Silver	Silver chromate	1×10^{-9}	10^{-6}
		Barium	Barium sulphate	3×10^{-8}	10^{-5}
		Potassium	Potassium cobaltinitrite	2×10^{-9}	10^{-5}
		Nickel	Nickel dimethylglyoxime	1×10^{-8}	10^{-5}
Colour		Iron	Iron (III) thiocyanate	2×10^{-9}	10^{-3}
		Chromium	Chromium (VI) diphenylcarbazide	3×10^{-12}	10^{-3}
Electrolysis	Platinum electrode	Copper	—	5×10^{-8}	10^{-3}
		Lead	Lead dioxide	5×10^{-7}	10^{-3}
	Mercury cathode	Iron	—	1×10^{-7}	10^{-3}
		Chromium	—	1×10^{-7}	10^{-3}

CHAPTER VI

QUANTITATIVE ANALYSIS

FOR the successful performance of a complete quantitative analysis of small samples, the ultramicrochemist must have at his command the complete array of the methods used in analytical chemistry. The operations performed in quantitative analysis are in general the same as those used in qualitative analysis (production of a precipitate, its separation from solution, heating, centrifuging, etc.). However, some additional techniques are inevitably needed as well, together with special apparatus and methods: these form the subject matter of the present chapter.

Valuable information on methods of quantitative analysis is to be found in Milton and Waters' book.* After the requisite modification of the apparatus, the methods there described may also be used in ultramicroanalysis.

BALANCES AND WEIGHING

To date, several works have been published on the direct weighing of quantities of the order of several micrograms, but only one describing methods of performing gravimetric analyses with ten micrograms of a substance. Evidently, this is a difficult problem, but it deserves attention, because it is often necessary in quantitative ultramicroanalysis to take portions of the substance to be analysed

It should be noted that in micro-,† and more so in ultramicro-analysis, it is, as a rule, desirable that the determination of an element

---

* R. MILTON and W. WATERS, *Methods of Quantitative Micro-Analysis*, London, 1955.

† I. P. ALIMARIN and B. I. FRID, *The Quantitative Microchemical Analysis of Minerals and Ores* (Kolichestvennyi mikrokhimicheskii analiz mineralov i rud), Goskhimizdat, Moscow, 1961.

should conclude, not with weighing of the isolated precipitate, but with some other operation, for example, photometry or electro-chemistry.

Ultramicrobalances

The first attempts at weighing quantities of the order of a micro-gram were made in 1882. Since that time several types of balances have been suggested for this purpose.

Torsion Balances

The simplest type of balance is the torsion balance, the principle of its construction is as follows. If a thin quartz, glass or metallic fibre is fixed at one end and loaded at the free end, the latter will drop depending on the load, the displacement being strictly propor-tional to the load for small loads. The magnitude of the displacement is given by Hooke's Law:

$$f = \frac{Pl^3}{3EJ}, \tag{13}$$

where f is the displacement of the end of the fibre in cm; P the applied load in kg; l the length of the fibre in cm; E the elastic modulus in kg/cm^2; J the moment of inertia.

The moment of inertia for a fibre of circular cross-section is:

$$J = \frac{\pi d^4}{64} \tag{14}$$

and, consequently,

$$f = \frac{64Pl^3}{3E\pi d^4} = \frac{6 \cdot 79Pl^3}{Ed^4} \tag{15}$$

For loads expressed in micrograms and displacements expressed in microns,

$$f = \frac{6 \cdot 79 \times 10^4 Pl^3}{10^9 Ed^4} = \frac{Pl^3}{14,700 \, Ed^4}$$

$$(1 \text{ cm} = 10^4 \, \mu, \, 1 \text{ kg} = 10^9 \, \gamma)$$

whence

$$l = \sqrt[3]{\left(\frac{14,700 \, Ed^4}{P}\right)}. \tag{16}$$

8

From this formula we may, for example, calculate the length of a quartz fibre of given diameter for which a given displacement corresponds to unit weight. The displacement of the end of the fibre is measured by a horizontal microscope whose focal length is about 10 mm and overall magnification × 50–100. The general appearance of this type of balance is shown in Fig. 35 with a detail

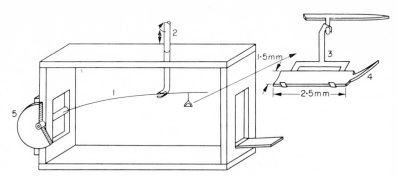

FIG. 35. General view of a torsion balance: 1—quartz fibre; 2—stop; 3—aluminium cradle; 4—platinum weighing tray; 5—mechanism for fixing and twisting the fibre.

showing the balance pan unit. The balance is very sensitive to small vibrations and also to air movements. The weighing is done in a special pan placed on a hanging cradle made of aluminium foil (see Fig. 35), which is permanently attached to the fibre.

Procedure: Bring the free end of the fibre, loaded only with the cradle and empty pan, into the centre of the field of view of the microscope by turning the knob at the fixed end. Then fix the balance by lowering the fibre on to the support catch. Remove the pan, place the sample to be weighed in it and then put the pan back on to the aluminium cradle. Next lower the stop carefully: the end of the fibre appearing in the field of view of the microscope will be displaced relative to its original position. By turning a micrometer screw, set the microscope in such a way that the end of the thread again appears in the centre of the field of view on the intersection of two mutually perpendicular lines. Note the number of divisions of the screw. Alternatively, if there is a micrometer scale in the microscope eyepiece, note the number of divisions of the eyepiece scale through which the end of the fibre has been displaced; in this case, the position of the microscope will not alter.

First weigh several known weights (for the preparation of small weights see below) and construct a graph from the data obtained: the number of divisions of the micrometer screw or of the eyepiece scale gives the magnitude of the load.* Here a more exact result than that obtained by reading directly from the graph may be obtained by calculating the load from the formula $P = f \cot \alpha$, where P is the load in gammas and f the displacement of the balance arm in microns. It should be remembered that the zero point alters slightly after each weighing. The zero point must, therefore, be

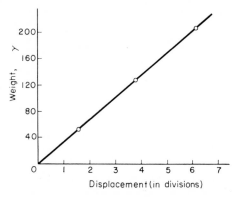

FIG. 36. Calibration curve for the balance.

established before each weighing, and the weight of the object determined as the difference between the position of the loaded and unloaded fibre.

On balances of the type described, tens and hundreds of micrograms of a substance may be weighed with a relative error of 3–5 per cent. The practical limit of the ratio of the maximum load and sensitivity of such balances is the length of the fibre which is not unlimited. Lengthening the thick quartz fibre leads to an increase in the maximum load without loss of sensitivity. However, a substantial increase in the length of the quartz fibre reduces the accuracy of the weighing.

Balances with a Quartz Arm

In quantitative ultramicroanalysis torsion balances find only limited application, because the total load (including tare weight)

* A straight line is obtained (Fig. 36) which can be used to establish the magnitude of the load by the displacement of the balance arm found.

that has to be weighed to give sufficient accuracy, is large compared with the net weight of the actual sample. Various types of balances with balance arms are, therefore, more widely used, the arm permitting the counterbalancing of a significant part of the load (the tare) by means of a counterweight. Precise weighing of very small samples can then be achieved. Descriptions of several kinds of

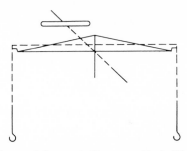

FIG. 37. Scheme of the quartz fibre assembly in Kirk's balance.

ultramicrobalances with balance arms are to be found in the literature [79–84]. We here describe two kinds that have best proved themselves in use under the conditions of ultramicroanalytical research.

Kirk, Craig, Gullberg and Boyer [85] have improved on Neher's simple torsional balance. Fused quartz fibres are used in the construction of this balance, which consists of a balance bar in the form of a cantilever beam soldered to a torsion fibre. The quartz fibre assembly is shown schematically in Fig. 37. The basic horizontal element of the balance arm is a quartz fibre of diameter about 200 μ and length 10 cm. Similar fibres are used for the vertical part of the balance arm and the short branch perpendicular to the plane of the arm, which provides the means of fixing the balance arm to the torsion fibre. The inclined fibres reinforcing the balance arm are 50–75 μ in diameter. There is also on the arm an indicator fibre of 15 μ dia. to enable the position of the arm to be determined. The height of the balance arm is 1 cm. To the ends of the arm are fixed fibres of about 5 μ dia., to which are soldered fibres of 50 μ dia. ending in hooks, from which the cradles for the scale pans may be hung. The arm is fixed in the middle to a torsion fibre, whose overall length is approximately 10 cm. (The sensitivity of the balance is determined fundamentally by the length and especially the diameter of the torsion fibre, being inversely proportional to the fourth power of the latter. The magnitude of the maximum load is approximately proportional to the square of the diameter. For a slight reduction in the diameter of the fibre, therefore, the increase in sensitivity achieved is greater than the reduction in the maximum load.) One

FIG. 38. Kirk's ultramicrobalance.

end of the fibre is attached to a graduated dial which is used to twist it, the other is fused to a rigid quartz rib, which is bow-shaped and ensures a constant tension in the fibre. The other end of the rib is fixed to a special mechanical device which may be used to change the tension and turn the fibre.

The whole quartz fibre mechanism is supported on a metal stand, which is fixed to the baseplate of the balance, and is enclosed in a case (Fig. 38).

The most important mechanical detail is the dial, which must be set up very precisely. The dial is divided into 2000 equal parts.

The optical system consists of two objectives $\times 3$, which are focused respectively on either end of the controlling quartz fibre, and a prism system, whereby images of the fibre ends are passed through the bottom of the protective case of the balance and fall into the two halves respectively of the field of view, being then projected by an objective $\times 7$ on to a square (10×10 cm) ground glass screen. The control fibre is thus projected in the form of two horizontal fibres: at the zero point both lines merge into one. The light source is two small lamps, whose light falls inside the balance and is focused by cylindrical lenses placed behind the control fibres. This type of balance can be used to weigh 0·3 mg and less of a substance with a sensitivity of 5×10^{-9} g for a total load (including the weight of the tray) of the order of several tenths of a gram. The most important limiting factor in weighing is the difficulty of supporting the weight of the object within the limits of sensitivity of the balance. Vibration has no noticeable effect on the sensitivity, because it is quickly damped by the rib to which the torsion fibre is fixed. The balance is very sensitive to dust, so the case must form a reliable protection. Temperature variations do not significantly affect the balance because quartz has a low temperature coefficient of expansion. The action of air currents, arising from the different temperatures of different parts of the balance, are levelled out by covering the balance with several cases with air layers between them.

Korenman, Fertel'meister and Rostokin [86] suggest the use of a torsion balance of somewhat different construction (Fig. 39). A light aluminium balance arm 1, weighing about 20 mg and made from a strip of aluminium foil 0·4 mm wide and 0·1 mm thick, is fixed with shellac or a cellulose nitrate varnish to the middle of a quartz fibre 2, whose diameter is about 20μ and length 100 mm. The fibre is inside a brass tube with a cut-out where the balance arm is attached. One end of the fibre is attached to a fixed bushing, the other to a movable bearing. On the axis of the bearing is fixed, by means of a cylinder and spring, a conical toothed wheel 3, which is used to twist the fibre. The tube with fibre and balance arm is placed on an iron stand 4, which is fixed on a lead plate for stability. Twenty millimetres below the tube and parallel to the balance arm is a copper plate 5 with two aluminium prisms at opposite ends to limit the travel of the arm. To observe the equilibrium position of the arm by the sight 6, which is made of phosphor bronze 10μ

thick, a horizontal microscope is fixed on the base plate. To avoid jerks, rotary motion is communicated to the fibre through a system of cogs (see Fig. 39). There is a scale and pointer on the axis of the lowest cog. With such an arrangement of cogs, a full revolution

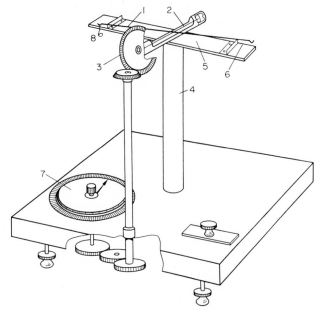

FIG. 39. Scheme of Korenman's ultramicrobalance.

of the pointer through 360° corresponds to torsion of the fibre through 180°.

The device is covered by a wooden box with four sections. In two, lying in the same plane, are the balance arm and the plate with the prisms, while the tube with the quartz fibre is in the other two, which lie in a plane perpendicular to the first. The width of each section is about 5·5 cm, so that the fibre and balance arm are within a very confined space; thus the effect of air currents is practically eliminated. With a fibre of 24·2 μ dia. the accuracy of weighing on the model described is 0·3 γ in units of weight. Oscillations of $\pm$0·5 divisions of the indicator scale occur. Therefore, to increase the accuracy, a fibre of smaller diameter should be used: increasing the accuracy of reading by complication of the cog system does not help.

Procedure. The weighing operation on torsional ultramicrobalances is carried out as follows.

Put the empty cups, whose weight must be practically identical, into the respective cradles. Switch on the light and wait till air movements have stopped. Release the cups and set the graduated wheel so that the images of the two ends of the control fibre (on Kirk's balance) merge into one unbroken line. Remove the cup to be used for the sample with a fork of platinum wire and load it; then replace. The loading and unloading must be done very precisely, otherwise the balance may be broken. After loading the balance, set the reading wheel so that the images of the ends of the control fibre coincide. Obtain the weight of the object by multiplying the difference between the two indications of the graduated dial before and after loading by the calibration coefficient.

The calibration of the torsional ultramicrobalance reduces to the determination of the relation between the weight of the sample and the corresponding indication of the reading wheel. Theoretically and experimentally this relation is linear. It is, therefore, sufficient to know only the magnitude of the calibration coefficient, by which the weight of the sample can be calculated from the indications of the reading wheel.

It is very difficult to prepare small weights for ultramicroweighing and also to use them, which makes a high degree of accuracy difficult to attain. At present the ultramicrochemist has three indirect methods of calibration at his disposal.

Method 1. Evaporate to dryness and weigh various small volumes of salt solution (non-hygroscopic and of strictly determinate concentration, for example, potassium chloride) of exactly known concentration. In this case, the accuracy of the calibration is 0·1–0·2 per cent and is determined by the precision with which the very small volumes of solution are measured and the accuracy with which the concentration of the initial solution was determined.

Method 2. On an ordinary microbalance weigh a long piece of platinum wire of strictly uniform diameter (or a piece of foil of regular form). Cut the wire up into short lengths, taking the weight of the pieces to be proportional to their length. In the case of foil, cut several small rectangles out of it and measure their length and breadth under a microscope. From the weight of the whole piece of foil, its area and the area of the small rectangles calculate their weight, which depends on their area. Thus the pieces of wire or foil are used as small weights and provide the data for the calibration curve. The results of two parallel calibrations normally coincide with an error of ±0·5 per cent.

Method 3. Place in the pan of the ultramicrobalance a grain of a pure substance (for example, potassium dichromate) which can be used for volumetric analysis, and note the displacement of the balance arm. Then dissolve the grain in a small volume and titrate it. Calculate the weight of the grain from the quantity of titrating agent used. Repeat this operation several times and construct the calibration graph from the data obtained.

Flotational Weighing

Besides the direct determination of the weight of small quantities of a substance, there are indirect methods depending on the calculation of the weight from the accurately determined volume and

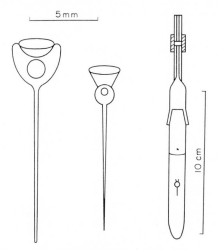

FIG. 40. The Cartesian diver.

specific gravity of the sample. A device used successfully for this purpose is the "Cartesian diver" [14]. In the diver (Fig. 40), which is loaded into the vessel with the liquid, there is a small air bubble. Any action causing a change in the volume of the gas bubble or in the total weight of the diver is detected with a high degree of sensitivity by the ensuing displacements of the diver in the vertical direction. These displacements are easily compensated by a change in the external pressure. To obtain the weight the behaviour of the diver when loaded with the sample is compared with its behaviour when loaded with small weights.

Flotational weighing has not been used in inorganic analysis to date; however, it can be used in some cases, when the substance to be weighed does not interact with the liquid used. A more detailed account of this method is to be found in Kirk's monograph [14].

Korenman and Fertel'meister [87] used the change in position of the meniscus of a viscous and non-volatile liquid in a capillary when a solid is lowered into it to determine the density of certain solids.

Examples of Gravimetric Determinations

Determination of the Specific Gravity [11]

To determine the specific gravity, place a small volume of the liquid in a glass capillary of about 0·1 mm dia. and about 0·3 γ capacity. Put

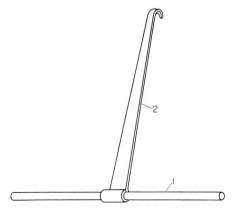

Fig. 41. Capillary (1) on the suspension device (2).

the capillary on the balance arm of an ultramicrobalance (here a torsion balance may be used) with the aid of a strip of aluminium foil about 0·1 mm thick (Fig. 41). First weigh the empty capillary, then successively the same capillary with equal volumes of water and the liquid in question. Divide the weight of the liquid by that of the water: the quotient gives the specific gravity of the liquid.

Notes. The capillary is conveniently filled with water and the liquid by micro-pipetting on the microscope stage: measure the length of the column by the eyepiece scale and thence calculate the volume. The capillary should not be held with anything other than tweezers. This method can be used to determine the specific gravity of liquids with low vapour tension which do not evaporate noticeably during the weighing.

Determination of the Dry Residue [11]

Measure a volume of liquid in a measuring capillary, transfer it to the weighing pan and leave in a desiccator till completely evaporated; then weigh. Determine the constancy of the weight of the dry residue by placing the pan in a drying cupboard at 40–50° for 10–15 minutes, cooling and again weighing. The evaporation on heating gives lower results, obviously, because of the removal of granules of the residue by the liquid vapour.

Determination of the Residue after Calcination [11]

Place a small amount of the substance to be analysed in the platinum weighing pan. Then put it in a large crucible, as shown in Fig. 42, to

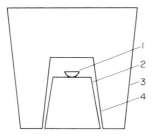

FIG. 42. Arrangement for putting a small sample in an oven: 1—platinum cup with sample; 2, 3, 4—crucibles.

reduce losses due to the removal of ash by convection currents. Put the large crucible in a crucible furnace at 400–600° for a few minutes, then draw it out of the furnace, allow it to cool in a desiccator and weigh the pan. For weights of 500–50 γ this method gives completely satisfactory results.

The Gravimetric Determination of Lead, Silver and Mercury

The examples given above cannot, strictly speaking, be classified as gravimetric determinations in the proper analytical sense. They provide rather an illustration of the use of the ultramicrobalance for single weighings. Below we describe a method of gravimetric analysis [89] which has been developed for the determination of lead, silver and iron; a Kirk balance of somewhat simplified construction is used [88].

All chemical operations are performed on the microscope stage with the aid of micromanipulators. It should be emphasized at this point that strict attention to every detail of the experiment is of particular importance: this includes the necessary treatment with anti-wetting agent of the pipette, swift and precise measurement of solutions and reagents, complete saturation of the moist chamber with water vapour and appropriate preparation of the capillary cones. The preliminary experiments on the calibration of the balance have made clear the necessity of taking three readings for each weighing.

Determination of lead. Choose two microcones of approximately equal weight, dry them at 340° for 10 min in a heating block in a drying capillary, then transfer them carefully to the holder in the moist chamber. Into one of the cones put a volume of about 200 mλ, measured accurately in a measuring capillary, of a solution containing 10 γ of lead, add an equal volume of 4 N sulphuric acid and then centrifuge vigorously. Wash the precipitate twice with distilled water, each time filling the cone almost completely. In doing this, do not disturb the precipitate, but allow it to remain in contact with the water for about 10 min each time. Then put the cone with the precipitate back in another drying capillary and into a heating block; desiccate at 100° for 10 min and then at 330–340° for 30 min. Weigh the lead sulphate precipitate, balancing out the tare with the other microcone. The results of ten determinations are given below:

$$\begin{array}{l}\text{Lead found, } \gamma \\ (10\,\gamma \text{ taken})\end{array} \left\{\begin{array}{lllll} 10\cdot13 & 10\cdot05 & 10\cdot21 & 10\cdot00 & 10\cdot05 \\ 9\cdot91 & 10\cdot08 & 10\cdot14 & 10\cdot01 & 9\cdot95 \end{array}\right\} \text{Mean } 10\cdot05$$

Error: 0·89%

Determination of silver. The procedure is to precipitate the silver in the form of its chloride, using 0·5 N hydrochloric acid as the precipitating agent and 0·01 N nitric acid as the washing solution. The instructions and technique are identical to those described for lead. Results:

$$\begin{array}{l}\text{Silver found, } \gamma \\ (10\,\gamma \text{ taken})\end{array} \left\{\begin{array}{lllll} 9\cdot94 & 10\cdot14 & 10\cdot03 & 10\cdot10 & 10\cdot13 \\ 9\cdot87 & 10\cdot08 & 10\cdot01 & 10\cdot20 & 10\cdot19 \end{array}\right\} \text{Mean } 10\cdot07$$

Error: 1·09%

Determination of mercury (I). The precipitate of the chloride is formed by treatment with a 0·5 N hydrochloric acid solution: the washing liquid used is water. The technique is analogous to that described above. Dry the empty microcone at 120° for 10 min. Dry the precipitate at $100°$ for 10 min and at $120°$ for 30 min, because there may be losses at higher temperatures.

$$\text{Mercury found, } \gamma \begin{cases} 9\cdot96 & 10\cdot07 & 10\cdot08 & 9\cdot98 & 9\cdot91 \\ 9\cdot90 & 10\cdot11 & 10\cdot05 & 10\cdot01 & 9\cdot85 \end{cases} \text{Mean } 9\cdot99$$

$(10 \gamma \text{ taken})$

Error: $0\cdot9\%$

The examples above show that for all three determinations, the drying is carried out at a temperature which ensures the complete removal of the precipitating agent and so simplifies the washing operation.

The accuracy of the determination is limited not by the actual weighing, but by the preliminary operations. It is, therefore, necessary to emphasize once again the need for care in these stages.

VOLUMETRIC METHODS

General Remarks

If volumetric determinations of several gammas of a substance are made on the microscale [90], that is, the work is done with significantly dilute solutions, there are, as is well known, several important shortcomings in such proceedings [11]. However, the same quantities of the substance may be determined with a greater degree of accuracy when the normal concentrations used in the macromethod are being analysed, provided that correspondingly small volumes are employed. Ultramicroanalysis is the method which makes this possible.

Only one study, by Benedetti-Pichler [33] has been published on the problem of visual ultramicrotitration with the aid of the microscope and manipulators.

There are only two papers [45, 46] describing electrical methods of determining the endpoint of a titration on the ultramicroscale.

Volumetric ultramicroanalytical methods are used chiefly for the determination of the fundamental components of very small samples of solids or solutions. Thanks to the fact that they are used in other methods too, the techniques used in volumetric determinations (transfer of solution from one vessel to another, precise measurement of small volumes, etc.) make the volumetric method fundamental and one of the most universal.

Because the analytical principles involved in ultramicroanalysis are no different from those used in the analysis of normal quantities, we must take into account on this scale too all data concerning the reliability, advantages and shortcomings of the method of analysis used.

In volumetric analyses involving titration the essential requirement, as is well known, is the exact determination of the end point of the titration, for the establishment of which a specific property of the system is used that changes sharply at this point. The indicators normally used for this purpose change colour, which is detected by eye, not at the equivalence point, but somewhat earlier or later: this is the origin of the titration error:

$$\text{T.E.} = \frac{a \times v}{N \times V} \tag{17}$$

where a is the sensitivity of the indicator in g-equiv./l., i.e., the concentration of ions of the substance being titrated in the solution which can cause a change in colour in the indicator: v the final volume of the titrated solution; N the normality of the solution to be titrated; V the initial volume of the solution to be titrated.

The reduction in quantity of the substance under investigation in volumetric ultramicroanalysis occurs as a result of the diminution of the volume used, while the normal concentrations of all the solutions used in the titration are maintained. Under these conditions, the titration error arises only in connexion with the chemical properties of the given system. It is, therefore, the same for any one method, independently of the scale on which the determination is made. At the same time, this error is significantly less on the ultramicro- than on the microscale, where comparatively dilute solutions are used.

On the other hand, the thinness of the liquid layer when small volumes are analysed, even with specially developed techniques of observation, require a higher concentration of the indicator if visual observation of the change in the system titrated is to be possible. Therefore the relative magnitude of the drop error, which is connected with the volume of the minimum portion of the reagent, the addition of which at the end of the titration causes a change in colour of the indicator, is significantly greater on the ultramicro-than on the macroscale: the quantity of reagent added for this purpose is a significant part of the whole volume. However, this error connected with the large amount of indicator present, may be taken into account by the introduction of a correction for the quantity of indicator and also by titration in the presence of a comparison. Further, to facilitate observation of the point when the indicator changes colour, a localization procedure is used in volumetric ultramicroanalysis: for example, the change is observed on particles of precipitate, fibres or a small drop of an organic liquid which is immiscible with the solution being titrated. But here too there are factors which make it difficult to obtain reproducible results. Thus, for example, when silk threads are used for localization of the indicator, the intensity of the colour is found to fall somewhat during the titration process for the following reasons.

1. Whitening. If a fibre soaked in methyl red is placed in an alkaline solution, the dye is extracted from the surface of the fibre; the red colouring of the fibre itself is not recovered thereafter.

2. Delayed action. At pH 8 the colour of the fibre takes 1–2 min to change.

3. Effect of the change of the pH of the medium. In buffer solutions silk fibres soaked with methyl red become red at pH 6, orange at pH 7 and yellow at pH 8. A woollen fibre in a 0·5 N solution of potassium hydroxide remains red.

When one of the reacting substances plays the part of the indicator, the experimenter must take into account the need to use more concentrated solutions, which brings in its train an increase in the drop error—for which an exact allowance cannot always be made.

The normal random errors of the volumetric method affect the results of determinations differently when small volumes of solutions are used; in this connexion there arise a number of additional systematic errors. Thus, temperature variations have considerably greater effect than in microanalysis. Another factor of great importance is the moisture of the surrounding atmosphere: on this largely depends the rate of evaporation of the solvent from the solution, the rate being in any case higher for small volumes because of the high ratio of free surface to volume.

Leakage error, which increases with reduction in the diameter of the burette and becomes very large in microanalysis, does not, as such, exist in volumetric ultramicroanalysis, where horizontal burettes are used. But there is an error connected with the rate of flow of the solution—the higher the latter, the more solution is left on the walls of the horizontal burettes.

Of particular importance in work with small volumes is their accurate measurement, with which is linked the reading error. Correct choice of burette diameter allows this error to be significantly reduced. According to the data of Korenman [11] and Benedetti-Pichler [33], the formula to be used in choosing burette diameter is the following:

$$d = 50.5 \sqrt{\frac{\varepsilon}{NP}} \tag{18}$$

where ε is the relative error of the reading, N the normality of the standard solution, P the ratio of the number of γ-equiv. of the substance to be titrated in microanalysis (which is taken to be equal to 40,000 γ-equiv.) to the number of γ-equiv. in ultramicroanalysis. This formula is to be used together with Table 11, which

TABLE 11. CHOICE OF BURETTE DIAMETER

$\pm\varepsilon$, %	Length of burette, mm	Number of γ-equiv. to be titrated					
		Up to 0·04 γ-equiv. ($\sim$10 γ) $P = 10^6$			Up to 0·004 γ-equiv. ($\sim$1 γ) $P = 10^7$		
		Normality and volume of the standard solution used					
		1 N, 0·04 λ	0·1 N, 0·4 λ	0·01 N, 4 λ	0·1 N, 0·04 λ	0·01 N, 0·4 λ	0·001 N, 4 λ
0·5	40	0·035	0·11	0·35	0·035	0·11	0·35
1·0	20	0·05	0·16	0·50	0·05	0·16	0·5

gives the diameter of the burette (in mm) in relation to a series of the factors taken into account by formula (18).

The table shows that in volumetric ultramicroanalysis it is appropriate to use for the calibrated part of the burette, capillary tubes of 0·03–0·5 mm internal diameter.

The need to move the meniscus slowly during the titration makes it essential that the aperture at the end of the burette be very fine. The use of such a burette is made easier by the action of the surface forces, which are considerable in capillaries: in fact, they make it possible to dispense with taps. The burette is fitted with a device for controlling the air pressure above the standard solution in it. The air pressure is balanced by the surface tension of the solution in the burette. When a gravity arrangement is used, the air pressure over the standard solution is arranged so that, when the tip of the burette is dipped into the solution, the latter can either flow out of or fill the burette. In the first case the pressure is somewhat greater, in the second somewhat smaller, than $2\sigma/r$, where σ is the surface tension of the solution and r the radius of the burette at the meniscus. The accuracy attainable with such a burette depends essentially on the magnifying power of the microscope objective and the eyepiece micrometer scale, since these last determine the number of divisions of the eyepiece scale and, consequently (for a given burette diameter), the volume of solution corresponding to each division. The volume of the graduated part of the burette is generally about 0·05 λ.

The choice of an appropriate vessel for the titration is more difficult than that of the burette, because some of the requirements are directly contradictory: the volume of solution must be small, but the layer deep (to allow observation of the change of colour of the indicator at the end-point of the titration); at the same time the diameter of the vessel must be large enough to allow mixing of the solution and the immersion of the burette tip. As a review of the work in this field shows, research workers have used indicators adsorbed on to solid particles of a porous substance. Mixing of the solution has been achieved by turbulent motion—which can be observed in a drop of the solution being titrated if it is moved along the capillary tube [33] or by a gas jet [45].

In ultramicroanalysis, standard solutions are prepared in smaller quantities than in macroanalysis, but not in too small quantities (5–10 ml), since changes in the titre of a solution are large in the case of small quantities, because of evaporation or solubility of the glass. At the same time it should be remembered that, to obtain true results, the normality of the working solution used in calculation

9

must be that determined by the titration of a corresponding volume of standard solution.

The methods and technique of volumetric ultramicroanalysis have been developed to the end that the systematic errors arising from the inadequacies of the apparatus shall not be significantly greater than the errors in microanalysis. However, it is considerably more difficult to prepare and use apparatus for measuring small volumes with greater accuracy than apparatus for conventional volumes. It is, therefore, always necessary to seek a compromise between accuracy and convenience of working. The order of magnitude of the limiting error in the majority of volumetric determinations in ultramicroanalysis is not greater than ± 0.5 per cent.

Visual Titration

Apparatus [33]

Titration in volumes of 2–1 λ or less is done in the moist chamber on the microscope stage.

The titration vessel in this case is a micropipette tip which is somewhat wider and shorter than usual (diameter 0.2 mm, length 3–5 mm). A capillary vessel of overall length about 10 cm is fixed in a piston device in which the meniscus of the hydraulic fluid is about 2 cm from the tip. This piston device is used for mixing: as the drop of the solution being titrated moves along the capillary, turbulence arises in it which ensures complete mixing, if the drop is moved to and fro through 0.15–1 mm four or five times. The piston device with the vessel is fixed in the left manipulator.

The burette is a capillary of internal diameter about 0.5 mm, whose tip is drawn out to a diameter of about 20 μ. Such burettes are made of thick-walled glass tubes, external diameter 6–8 mm and internal diameter 2–4 mm.

Wash the tubes in hot chromic acid, twice distilled water, and ethyl alcohol, dry and then draw out in the flame of a blow-torch to capillaries, which are then cut into pieces 12–15 cm long.

The burette tips are drawn out in a quartz micro-oven; this is a quartz tube of 2–3 mm dia., 15–20 mm length, wound with 6–7 turns of nichromel wire of 0.3 mm dia., insulated with asbestos thread and put into a porcelain tube 10–15 mm long. The ends of the nichrome winding are brought out of the tube some 10–15 mm and clamped with terminal nuts, to which the current leads are soldered: a 12 V a.c. power supply is provided by an auto-transformer and a step-down transformer, power is provided by alternating current, which passes through an auto-transformer (LATR-1) and a transformer (120 to 12 V). The body of the oven is clamped to a stand.

To draw out the capillary tip 1, lower it into the oven 2, holding the upper end of the capillary in a clamp 3 on the stand (Fig. 43). Fix the lower

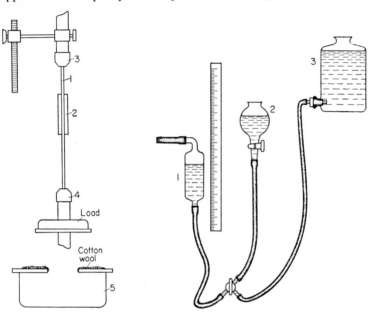

FIG. 43. Scheme of the apparatus for making burettes.

FIG. 44. Gravity arrangement.

end of the capillary, which should protrude from the oven far enough that this part makes up the length of the burette (10–12 cm), in a clamp with a disc 4, on which place a weight. Accurately under the lower clamp place a base 5, with a round collar with padded sides and opening: the diameter must be somewhat less than the diameter of the disc of the lower clamp. The construction of the clamps is analogous to those used for fixing the pipettes in the piston device.

Switch on the oven heat to redness. After some time the capillary will soften and fall under the weight of the load, coming to rest on the collar of the base. The capillary with a drawn-out tip this obtained is the burette. Release it from the lower clamp, check the uniformity of the internal diameter under a microscope and store in a cylinder with a cover ground to fit on the outside.

Before use mark the portion of the burette that is uniform in diameter with a ring made of a fine hair of Canada Balsam, Gliptal or BF glue. Draw out the hair by touching the mass of the substance with a glass rod and by lifting the rod quickly. Fix the burette in the body of a micropipette holder, the opposite end of which serves as the connexion to the gravity arrangement [33, 45].

The gravity arrangement (Fig. 44) provides positive or negative pressure in the space (vessel—rubber tube—inner part of the burette) which serves as a buffer in the transmission of pressure to the solution in the burette. The whole system is filled with water in such a way that, when the uppermost vessel 3 is shut off, the intercommunicating vessels 1 and 2 are half full. The vessels 1 and 2 are fixed on stands with a racking gear so that they can be displaced relative to one another in the vertical direction. The positive or negative pressure created in this system either counteracts or reinforces the surface forces of the solution in the burette until the tip of the burette is in the solution.

If a definite volume is to be measured out under these conditions, the mark on the burette must be in the field of view of the microscope.

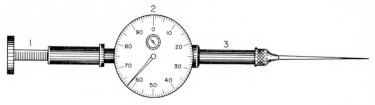

Fig. 45. Burette with micrometer.

This is not always convenient because it prevents the simultaneous observation of the titration vessel in the field of view of the microscope. A burette has, therefore, been constructed [45] that works on the principle of the micropipette in qualitative ultramicroanalysis [48], but also takes into account the possibility of precise measurement of solutions. The system is shown in Fig. 45: between the microscrew 1 and the holder 3 there is a micrometer 2, whose moving part works like a piston in a holder. In this case, when the burette is filled or emptied, the number of divisions through which the pointer on the micrometer dial moves as the screw is turned correspond to a definite volume of solution, which may easily be determined by calibration. It should be noted that the diameter of the piston must be substantially reduced (to 1 mm), because otherwise one division on the dial will correspond to too large a volume of solution in the burette.

Calibration of the burette. Set the moist chamber, with a vessel containing distilled water and a measuring capillary, on the microscope stage. In the chuck of the right manipulator fix a holder with a burette that has already been marked. Connect the free end of the holder to the air pressure regulating apparatus with rubber tubing (Fig. 44).

Bring the distilled water vessel into the field of view of the microscope, then bring up the burette tip to the mouth of the vessel. Next move both together without letting the burette tip touch the meniscus of the solution until the mark on the burette comes into the field of view. With the three-way tap in the regulating apparatus shut, move the water vessel on to the burette tip and watch the movement of the meniscus in the burette under the microscope: this movement can be stopped at any time by drawing the tip of the burette out of the liquid. Next, turn the three-way tap so that vessels 1 and 2 may intercommunicate and find their correct position relative to one another, so that the water begins to flow at the desired rate from the tip of the burette when immersed in the liquid (first position). Note this mutual disposition of the two vessels on the centimetre scale next to the stand. In the first position, the flow of solution stops as soon as the burette tip is brought out of the solution into the air. To make the first drop of water flow out of the burette tip into the air, find the mutual disposition of the vessels 1 and 2 in which the difference between their levels is greater, because now the surface tension of two menisci is to be overcome—in the burette and at its tip (second position). If the burette is to be emptied completely into the air, then turn the three-way tap so that vessels 1 and 3 are connected to one another.

When the pressure needed for the system has been established, repeat the manipulations required to bring the mark on the burette into the field of view, but this time note the division of the eyepiece micrometer behind the mark at which the meniscus in the burette is seen. Without opening the three-way tap, put the vessels 1 and 2 in the second position. Remove the burette from the field of view and bring under the microscope the measuring capillary, whose diameter is close to that of the burette. Bring the burette tip up towards the capillary, then, moving the latter away, move the former on to the latter until the meniscus in the burette appears in the field of view. Note the position of the mensicus relative to the mark ' and observe its movement. When the meniscus approaches the desired division of the micrometer eyepiece scale, put the vessels 1 and 2 in the first position and draw the burette tip out of the liquid, at the same time noting the new position of the meniscus relative to the mark. Immediately bring the measuring capillary into the field of view and measure the length of the column of water in it. Then calculate the volume of water in the burette to which one division of the eyepiece scale corresponds. The following is a convenient way of writing down this information:

Capillary		Burette	
Number of divisions	Volume, λ	Number of divisions	Volume corresponding to one division

To calibrate the micrometer burette, set the moist chamber on the microscope stage with the distilled water vessel and measuring capillary as above. Fix the burette in the clamp of the right manipulator. Bring the water vessel into the field of view, move the burette tip up to it and, without allowing it to enter the water, move the vessel away and the burette after it until the mark on the burette appears in the field of view and reaches the middle. By turning the screw 1 (see Fig. 45), create a pressure in the burette and, observing with the naked eye, dip the tip in the water by moving the vessel towards the burette. Draw a quantity of water out of the vessel by turning the screw gradually so that a negative pressure is created in the burette, and watch the movement of the meniscus under the microscope. When the meniscus reaches the last division of the eyepiece micrometer scale, stop turning the microscrew. Note precisely the position of the meniscus relative to the mark as given by the eyepiece scale. Turn the screw so that the pointer of the micrometer moves through one division: this creates a definite pressure in the burette and expels a definite quantity of water into the vessel. Note the new position of the meniscus in the burette. Repeat this operation several times and calculate the mean number of divisions of the eyepiece scale corresponding to one division of the micrometer. Then calibrate the burette with the aid of the measuring capillary as described above (with the one difference that the work of the piston is used to move the water into and out of the burette). First calculate the volume in the burette corresponding to one division of the eyepiece micrometer, and then the volume expelled or drawn in by the movement of the pointer of the micrometer through one division on the dial.

Titration

When ordinary indicators are used, the sharp colour transition at the end point of the titration can be observed only if the depth of the solution exceeds 40 mm. In ultramicroanalysis, therefore, the indicator is localized on fibres or precipitates. In this case, the change of colour occurs at the surface, where it is easily observed under the microscope. In particular, for acidimetric or alkalimetric titrations silk fibres, coloured with methyl red, can be used. In the titration of a base with an acid, a mixture of potassium iodide, potassium iodate and starch has been used successfully as the indicator system [33].

In argentometric determinations, adsoprtion indicators [33] are used, in particular dichlorofluorescein and eosin (tetrabromo-fluorescein). The dispersion agent used in this case is dextrin.

The titration is done in a moist chamber open at both sides: inside on the holder are microvessels containing distilled water, the standard solution and the solution to be titrated. Bring the titration vessel into the field of view, fill it with the solution to be titrated, add the indicator and titrate. The operations are similar to those carried out in the calibration of the burette.

Examples of Determinations

The titration of acids and bases. Procedure. To 5 ml of a 0·5 M solution of sodium hydroxide add two drops each of 0·1 M solutions of iodide and potassium iodate and also ten drops of a 1 per cent starch solution. Fill one of the vessels in the holder with this solution and then transfer a definite volume of it to the titration vessel. Titrate with a 0·25 M sulphuric acid solution.

Argentometric titration. Procedure. Prepare large volumes of the solutions to be titrated.

(1) To 25 ml of a 0·1 M sodium bromide solution add 0·5 ml of 2 per cent dichlorofluorescein solution (sodium salt) and 2·5 ml of 2 per cent dextrin solution.

(2) To 25 ml of a 0·1 M sodium bromide solution, add 0·5 ml 2 per cent eosin solution and 2·5 ml 2 per cent dextrin solution.

Fill the vessels in the holder in the moist chamber with these solutions and then titrate them in turn, putting a definite volume into the titration vessel. Titrate with 0·1 M silver nitrate solution. The end point is determined by the observation of the colour of silver chloride (bromide) particles in reflected light.

Potentiometric Titration

The use of indicators in volumetric ultramicroanalysis involves a number of errors in the determination of the end point of the titration, as has been mentioned above.

When electrical methods are used to determine the end point of the titration, both the titration error and the drop error may be significantly reduced. These methods offer the additional advantage that dilute solutions, both those to be analysed and the standards, may be used in amperometric, conductometric or potentiometric titrations.

Potentiometric changes are particularly convenient because it is

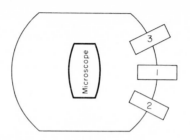

FIG. 46. Schematic position of the manipulators (1, 2, 3) in potentiometric titration.

possible to observe changes in the ion concentration during the titration process.

Apparatus

The procedure requires three manipulators, placed on the right of the microscope, as shown in Fig. 46.

The apparatus for titrating small volumes potentiometrically differs from that used for large quantities only in the part where the actual process of titration is carried out. The electrical circuit for measuring potentials remains unchanged.

We describe below a cell with platinum and calomel electrodes. In principle, similar apparatus can be used for the most varied determinations, different electrodes being employed as appropriate.

The potentiometric ultramicrotitration vessel is a capillary of 1–2 mm dia.: into it is fused a platinum wire with both ends free, one serving as the electrode, the other being soldered to a thin wire lead which goes to the potentiometer.

Construction. Prepare the vessel in the flame of a microburner; fuse the platinum wire into a capillary and then cut it off so that the working part of the vessel is 3–4 mm long (Fig. 47.1).

Split in half (lengthwise) a thick-walled capillary with internal diameter approximately equal to the diameter of the vessel. Put some plasticine in the glass holder thus obtained and press the vessel on to it. Then fix

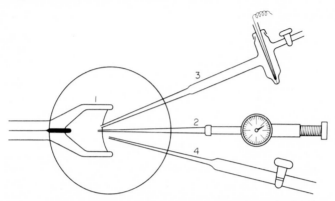

FIG. 47. General view of the cell used in potentiometric titration: 1—vessel with indicator electrode; 2—burette; 3—calomel electrode; 4—mixing gas supply.

the holder in its turn in the moist chamber, bringing the lead out through a hole in the wall.

The calomel comparison electrode is a small test-tube to which is fused a glass tube 150 mm long, 7 mm in external diameter, 2 mm in internal diameter, with its end drawn out into a capillary of 1·5–2 mm diameter and finishing in a fine tip of 0·05–0·1 mm dia. (Fig. 47, 3).

On the other side an outlet tube with a tap is fused to the test-tube. Put a drop of mercury and calomel on the bottom of the test-tube, then fill it and the glass tube with a potassium chloride solution.

Contact with the potentiometer is normally effected by a platinum wire fused into the glass tube of the test-tube cover.

Filling the calomel electrode. Fix the electrode in one of the manipulators. Put in a drop of mercury, then the calomel paste, prepared in the normal way, close the test-tube and join the outlet pipe to a water-pump. In a manipulator on the other side of the microscope, place a tube containing the potassium chloride solution. Moving the manipulators towards one another, immerse the tip of the calomel electrode in the solution; then open the tap in the outlet pipe and turn on the water-pump. As soon as

10

the solution fills the pipe and half the test-tube, close the tap; then, without taking the tip of the electrode out of the solution, disconnect the water pump and release the pressure: then draw the tip out of the solution and suck into it similarly a hot agar-agar solution. Draw the tip of the electrode out of the agar-agar only after the agar-agar has set.

Mixing of the solution during titration is conveniently achieved by means of a nitrogen jet, transmitted by a tube of 5–7 mm dia.; the flow is adjusted with a tap. The end of the tube is a capillary with a drawn-out tip like a pipette (Fig. 47, 4).

The burette used in potentiometric titration has been described in the section devoted to visual titration. It should only be emphasized that it is far more convenient and simple to use a micrometer burette.

Titration

Set the moist chamber on the microscope stage with the titration vessel and other apparatus required. Fix the burette in the middle and the calomel electrode and mixing gas tube on either side. First treat all the glassware with an anti-wetting agent. After adding the solution to be titrated, rotate the stage to bring the titration vessel in line with the mixing gas tube; mix with a nitrogen jet without letting the tip of the capillary enter the solution—the mixing is effected by the turbulence caused throughout the whole volume by the jet striking the surface of the solution, an effect which may be seen distinctly under the microscope. After mixing the solution, turn the chamber so that its open side is towards the calomel electrode and the tip of the latter is in line with the vessel; then dip the tip into the solution and make the measurement. Repeat the steps described until the titration is finished.

Potentiometric Ultramicrodeterminations

The determination of oxidizing and reducing agents. Prepare solutions of known concentration in 5-ml measuring flasks, fill the vessels in the moist chamber, transfer a definite volume of the solution to be titrated into the titration vessel and make the determination as described above. This procedure may be used to titrate 0·1 and 0·01 N solutions of ferrous ammonium sulphate, dichromate and vanadate: in a volume of 1–2 λ, 10^{-6} to 10^{-7} g of an element can be determined.

The results of such titrations are shown in Tables 12–14; some of the results are also shown graphically in Figs. 48–50.

The determination of the chloride ion [91]. If the platinum electrode in the titration vessel is covered with electrolytic silver and then with a silver chloride coating, it will serve as the indicator electrode for the chloride ion.

The electrode is silvered in the moist chamber in 5 hours at a current of 2 mA/cm^2, a single silver electrode serving as the anode. Then the vessel

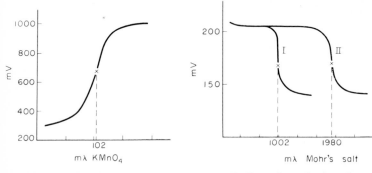

FIG. 48. Potentiometric ultramicro-determination of iron in Mohr's salt.

FIG. 49. Potentiometric ultramicro-determination of chromium in potassium dichromate: I—1×10^{-3} ml; II—2×10^{-3} ml.

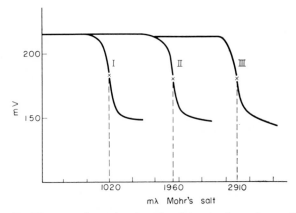

FIG. 50. The potentiometric ultramicrodetermination of vanadium in ammonium vanadate: I—1×10^{-3} ml; II—2×10^{-3} ml; III—3×10^{-3} ml.

with the silvered electrode is filled with 0·1 N hydrochloric acid; it is then electrolysed for 15 minutes at a current of 5–7 mA/cm^2 with the silvered electrode as anode and the single platinum electrode as cathode. The comparison electrode is made from mercury, mercury sulphate and sulphuric acid (2 N).

Put into the titration vessel an exactly measured volume of 0·01 N chloride solution, add sulphuric acid (final concentration about 0·02 N), and titrate with a 0·01 N silver nitrate solution.

The results are shown in Table 15 and the curves in Fig. 51.

TABLE 12. RESULTS OF THE POTENTIOMETRIC DETERMINATION OF IRON

Standard solution			Solution to be titrated, Mohr's salt		Quantity of iron, g		Err %
Solution	Concentration, N	Quantity used, ml	Volume ml	Concentration, N	Taken	Found	
$K_2Cr_2O_7$	0·01	1·99 × 10⁻³	2 × 10⁻³	0·01	1·12 × 10⁻⁶	1·11 × 10⁻⁶	−(
$K_2Cr_2O_7$	0·01	1·01 × 10⁻³	1 × 10⁻³	0·01	0·56 × 10⁻⁶	0·57 × 10⁻⁶	+)
$KMnO_4$	0·1	0·102 × 10⁻³	1 × 10⁻³	0·01	0·56 × 10⁻⁶	0·57 × 10⁻⁶	+)

TABLE 13. RESULTS OF THE POTENTIOMETRIC DETERMINATION OF CHROMIUM

Standard solution			Solution to be titrated, potassium dichromate		Quantity of chromium, g		Err %
Solution	Concentration, N	Quantity used, ml	Volume ml	Concentration, N	Taken	Found	
Mohr's salt	0·01	1·98 × 10⁻³	2 × 10⁻³	0·01	3·46 × 10⁻⁷	3·43 × 10⁻⁷	−)
Mohr's salt	0·01	1·01 × 10⁻³	1 × 10⁻³	0·01	1·73 × 10⁻⁷	1·74 × 10⁻⁷	+(
$Na_2S_2O_3$	0·1	0·76 × 10⁻³	1 × 10⁻³	0·01	2·91 × 10⁻⁶	3·0 × 10⁻⁶	+)

Amperometric Titration

The examples of potentiometric titration given above demonstrate that electrometric methods of determining the end point of a titration can be applied successfully to volumes of the order of 10^{-3} ml.

At the same time, it is well known that, for simplicity, accuracy, speed and sensitivity, the amperometric method is considerably superior to the potentiometric. The advantages of using this method

TABLE 14. RESULTS OF THE POTENTIOMETRIC DETERMINATION OF VANADIUM

Standard solution			Solution to be titrated, ammonium vanadate		Quantity of vanadium, g		Error, %
lution	Concentration, N	Quantity used, ml	Volume ml	Concentration, N	Taken	Found	
ohr's salt	0·01	$2·91 \times 10^{-3}$	3×10^{-3}	0·01	$1·53 \times 10^{-6}$	$1·48 \times 10^{-6}$	−3
ohr's salt	0·01	$1·96 \times 10^{-3}$	2×10^{-3}	0·01	$1·02 \times 10^{-6}$	$0·99 \times 10^{-6}$	−2
ohr's salt	0·01	$1·02 \times 10^{-3}$	1×10^{-3}	0·01	$5·1 \times 10^{-7}$	$5·22 \times 10^{-7}$	+2·3

TABLE 15. POTENTIOMETRIC DETERMINATION OF THE CHLORIDE ION

Standard solution			Chloride solution to be titrated		Quantity of chloride ions, g		Error, %
lution	Concentration, N	Quantity used, ml	Volume ml	Concentration, N	Taken	Found	
NO_3	0·01	$1·77 \times 10^{-3}$	$1·8 \times 10^{-3}$	0·01	$6·36 \times 10^{-7}$	$6·25 \times 10^{-7}$	−1·7
NO_3	0·01	$0·71 \times 10^{-3}$	$0·7 \times 10^{-3}$	0·01	$2·47 \times 10^{-7}$	$2·50 \times 10^{-7}$	+1·2

in microanalysis have been discussed repeatedly in the literature [92–94].

Kirk and his colleagues [95] in 1950 showed that a vibrating platinum electrode can be used in titrations in volumes of the order

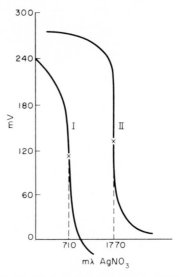

FIG. 51. Potentiometric ultramicrodetermination of the chloride ion: I—0.7×10^{-3} ml; II—1.8×10^{-3} ml.

of 10^{-2} ml to determine tens and units of a microgram of a substance without using the microscope and manipulators.

Below we describe the apparatus and method used for amperometric titration under the microscope.

Apparatus

Three manipulators are needed (Fig. 52), holding the vibrating platinum electrode, the comparison electrode and the burette respectively.

Procedure. To allow the simultaneous introduction into the moist chamber of three instruments, leave the chamber open on two sides and make a transverse slot in one of the side walls; the chamber bottom is thicker than usual in this case, so that the microvessels are higher than the guiding mechanism. Fix the vibrating platinum electrode, 0·2 mm in diameter and 2–3 mm long, in the manipulator 3 and introduce it into the moist chamber through the transverse slot; perpendicular to this, introduce the comparison electrode and a burette with its tip bent through 90°, placed respectively in the manipulators 2 and 1.

Titrate in an ordinary microvessel placed on the holder in the chamber. Also in the holder there are the vessels containing the standard solution and that to be titrated.

A saturated calomel electrode can be used as the comparison electrode and a micrometer burette for adding the standard solution.

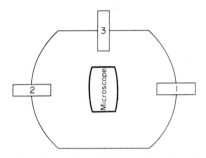

FIG. 52. Schematic position of the manipulators (1, 2, 3) for amperometric titration.

Before filling, treat all the glassware, including the comparison electrode, with an anti-wetting agent.

The vibration of the platinum electrode is effected by a bell; the hammer is bent back and an uninsulated lead is soldered to it. A ring at the other end of the lead is placed over the capillary of the vibrating electrode.*

Measure the current with a shunted galvanometer whose divisions are equivalent to $1·4 \times 10^{-8}$ A.

A general view of the cell and the electrical circuit are shown in Fig. 53.

The Titration

Bring the titration vessel into the field of view of the microscope and fill it with the aid of the pipette in manipulator 1 with a definite volume

---

* Alimarin and Gallai [96] have shown that, when a vibrating electrode is used in microanalysis, the current is proportional to the ion concentration to be determined.

of the solution to be titrated from the corresponding vessel (see above). Then replace the pipette in manipulator 1 with a burette. Withdraw the titration vessel from the field of view and introduce the platinum electrode along the centre up to the middle, placing on the left, at the same level as the tip of the electrode, the comparison electrode, and on the right, at the very edge of the field of view, the tip of the burette.

With the electrodes and burette thus arranged, move the vessel on to them, so that:

(1) the platinum electrode passes through almost all the solution,

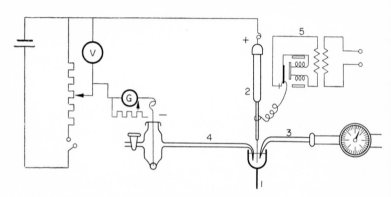

FIG. 53. General view of the cell and electric circuit for amperometric titration: 1—vessel with solution; 2—vibrating electrode; 3—burette; 4—calomel electrode; 5—vibrator.

but still lies free, not touching the walls of the vessel, the calomel electrode or the burette;

(2) the tip of the calomel electrode is sufficiently, but not too deeply, immersed in the solution; and

(3) the burette enters the solution along the wall.

After connecting up the electrical circuit (without connecting to the accumulator) and arranging the apparatus as described, switch on the vibrator and finally adjust the position of the platinum electrode so that it vibrates freely and fairly in the solution. Then join up to the accumulator and establish the voltage needed for the titration with the rheostat.

Use the burette to add the standard solution out of the vessel (see above), noting the deviation of the galvanometer and the corresponding volume on the burette dial; check the position of the apparatus under the microscope from time to time, and withdraw the calomel electrode as the volume increases. After the first noticeable deviation of the galvanometer pointer, note another four to five readings of the instrument and draw a graph.

Amperometric Ultramicrodeterminations

The apparatus described may be used for amperometric determination by the oxidation-reduction method of, for example, the system V(V)–Fe(II) by diffusion current of Fe^{2+} at $+1\cdot0$ V.

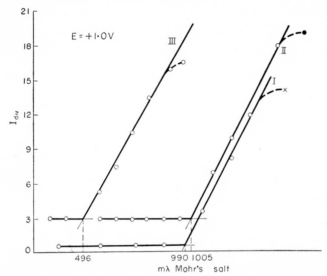

FIG. 54. The amperometric ultramicrotitration of ammonium vanadate with Mohr's salt at $E = 1\cdot0$ V: I—1 $\times$ 10^{-3} ml 0·01 N; II—1 $\times$ 10^{-3} and III—0·5 $\times$ 10^{-3} ml 0·001 N.

The results obtained are given in Table 16 and graphically in Fig. 54.

It is obvious that other systems can be titrated on the principles described with other electrodes.

When more dilute solutions are used (which is possible in principle for amperometric titration), correspondingly smaller quantities of a substance can be determined.

pH Measurement with a Glass Electrode

The pH of volumes of solutions of the order of 10^{-3} ml can be measured with the apparatus described below.

Make a *glass electrode* from a capillary of about 1 mm dia., drawn from a tube of special glass.

Take a piece of the capillary about 20 mm long and draw out the end in a microburner so that it tapers to a diameter of 0·3 mm in a length of about 10 mm; then seal the broad end. Reduce the flame as much as possible and seal the other end of the capillary, holding it in the flame till a sphere is formed. During heating, remove the excess of molten glass from the end of the sphere with another capillary.

Use a micropipette to fill the glass electrode thus obtained with 1 N hydrochloric acid, and then place it in an ampoule that can be sealed with the same acid; leave the electrode there for a week. When filling the glass electrode, note that the acid will not pass into the sphere immediately, but remain in the capillary. To fill the sphere, introduce the pipette into it and draw out some air: the negative pressure thus produced will draw the acid into the space. At the end of the week, wash the electrode carefully with water and leave it in water for 24 hr; then fill with a special solution.

Connect the electrode up to the potentiometer as follows: solder a thin lead to a plated wire and pass the latter through an ebonite holder, so that only part of the length of the lead appears on the other side of the holder. Solder a platinum wire about 20 mm long to the lead, then cover the lead with a capillary and introduce the platinum wire into the electrode: attach the capillary part of the electrode to the capillary covering the lead with picein. Join the other end of the plated wire to the potentiometer through a contact coupling.

Make the *calomel electrode* as described above and join it to the potentiometer with a thin wire, this too ending in a contact coupling. Any suitable potentiometer may be used for the measurement.

TABLE 16. TITRATION OF AMMONIUM VANADATE WITH FERROUS AMMONIUM SULPHATE

Voltage V	Standard solution of Mohr's salt		Vanadate solution to be titrated		Quantity of vanadium, g		Error %
	Concentration, N	Quantity used, ml	Concentration, N	Volume ml	Taken	Found	
+1·0	0·01	$0·99 \times 10^{-3}$	0·01	1×10^{-3}	$5·10 \times 10^{-7}$	$5·06 \times 10^{-7}$	−0·9
	0·001	$4·96 \times 10^{-4}$	0·001	5×10^{-4}	$2·55 \times 10^{-8}$	$2·53 \times 10^{-8}$	−0·8
	0·001	$1·005 \times 10^{-3}$	0·001	1×10^{-3}	$5·10 \times 10^{-8}$	$5·12 \times 10^{-8}$	+0·3

The *cell* (Fig. 55) consists of a capillary (3) placed in the moist chamber, with the glass (1) and calomel (2) electrodes introduced into it from either side; the electrodes are fixed on holders in manipulators on the left and right respectively.

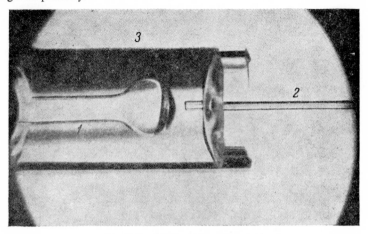

FIG. 55. Cell with glass ultramicroelectrode.

Tests comparing the data obtained with a glass microelectrode on buffer solutions with standard glass electrodes give the following results.

TABLE 17. MEASUREMENT OF pH WITH A GLASS ELECTRODE

pH value		pH value	
Standard electrode	Micro-electrode	Standard electrode	Micro-electrode
2·17	2·30	5·40	5·45
2·90	2·98	7·80	7·70
3·75	3·80	8·88	8·70
4·45	4·45		

COLORIMETRIC METHODS

It is well known that colorimetric methods are generally somewhat less accurate than gravimetric and volumetric methods. Frequently, however, they are more sensitive while being sufficiently reliable.

In ultramicroanalysis, the usual instruments (colorimeters, photometers, spectrophotometers) are used for colorimetric determinations: they need only to be adapted for work with small volumes.

The question of the smallest determinable quantity of a substance and also that of the use of the Bouguer–Lambert–Beer law in work with small volumes have been discussed in detail above (see p. 33).

In the present chapter, therefore, we need discuss only the construction of the cuvettes and other instruments used in making colorimetric ultramicrodeterminations.

Apparatus

Cuvettes

In normal cuvettes the light beam is absorbed only by an inconsiderable part of the solution, the remainder absorbing no light. If, however, the internal diameter of the cuvette used is not greater than the diameter of the light beam, so long as the layer of solution is thick enough to make analysis possible, the quantity of the substance can be made small and the whole will absorb light. Thus the quantity of a substance needed for colorimetric measurements can be reduced to the smallest amount that is absolutely needed for making the determination.

In this connexion many well-known types of cuvette have been devised on the principle of using thick-walled tubes with a small internal diameter. In the simplest case, these are pieces of capillary tubing of various lengths, diameters and, consequently, capacities. For example, Somogyi's microcolorimeter (described below) uses as cuvettes capillary beakers 20 mm long with a capacity of 10 λ. Capillary tubing is used also with other types of microcolorimeter [97–99]. On the same principle, Kirk and his colleagues have devised a capillary cuvette made of Teflon [14] (Fig. 56). Small windows made of glass, quartz or transparent plastic, are screwed on to the ends of the cuvette. The capacity of those used by the authors was 160–200 λ, their length being about 5 cm and internal diameter 2 mm. On this principle Kirk later [97] made a smaller glass cuvette of 20 λ capacity (diameter 0·7 mm, length 5 cm).

Another type of cuvette is similar to the normal type of rectangular cuvette, except that the side walls are thickened; the space occupied by the liquid is 1–2 mm wide. The advantage of such cuvettes is that the normal base can be used with them, because their external dimensions are similar to the normal type. A cuvette of this type measuring $2 \times 10 \times 25$ mm has a capacity of 500λ. If the light

Fig. 56. Teflon capillary cuvette.

beam is passed through suitable diaphragms, the capacity of such a cuvette may be brought down to 50λ; if the width of the space occupied by the solution is 1 mm, the capacity can be reduced to 30λ.

The filling of these small cuvettes with solution presents a special problem. In the vertical position, a capillary cuvette can be filled with a micropipette with a bent tip (see p. 35). Kirk's cuvette is filled from above through one of the openings in front of the windows. Normally, such cuvettes are filled by means of capillaries with a drawn-out tip. Koch [100] suggests that a single method of filling should be used for all capillary cuvettes, as follows.

Take a thick-walled capillary 1, exactly equal in diameter to the cuvette: grind one end flat and draw the other to a fine tip (Fig. 57, II), the length of the tip depending on the size of the vessel containing the solution. Press the capillary firmly against the bottom of the cuvette with springs. Similarly, press a glass cap 2 on the top and thus link to the cuvette a pneumatic device 3, consisting of a rubber bulb and a micrometer screw. For filling, fix the cuvette in a stand with a racking gear and suck in solution until it appears in part 2. Then take off the capillary 1, squeeze out a little of the solution and then put the window cap on carefully, turning the cuvette bottom up. Reverse the cuvette once more, remove part 3 and cover the second window. When acids and neutral solutions are used, the cuvette may be treated with methylchlorsilane anti-wetting agent: thanks to this, the drop squeezed out before the window is placed in position does not spread out over the whole surface, so that the excess (above that needed for filling and making the measurement) volume of solution is not large.

It is, however, obvious that this method of filling the cuvette requires the availability of a considerable excess (by comparison with the volume of the cuvette proper) of the solution to be analysed,

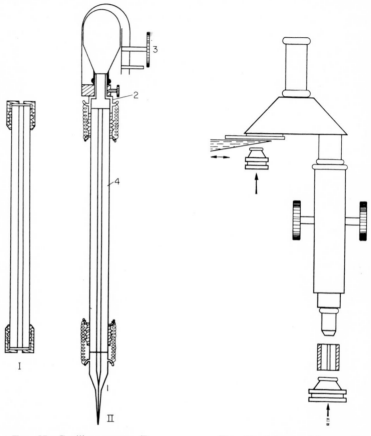

FIG. 57. Capillary cuvette (I) with filling device (II).

FIG. 58. Scheme of Somogyi's microcolorimeter.

because, besides the cuvette, parts 1 and 2 have to be filled as well (see Fig. 57).

Instruments

The majority of the well-known instruments cannot be used

without alteration for making colorimetric determinations with very small volumes of a liquid.

A convenient type of microcolorimeter has been suggested by Somogyi [101, 102]. In this instrument the microscope is combined with an optical device, by which the light beams are brought into a single field of view by prisms. The instrument is shown schematically in Fig. 58. The light beam, on passing through the solution to be analysed, is focused by the objective of a microscope whose eyepiece has been removed and then brought into the one field of view of the normal prism system, as used in Dubosq's colorimeter. The standard solution is put on the other side immediately in front of the wedge. The light beam is focused by the microscope condenser, after which it passes through an iris diaphragm and an optical wedge, and is finally brought into the field of view by prisms. The illumination of the two halves of the field of view is balanced by varying the position of the optical wedge.

There are also other well-known types of colorimeter involving the use of the microscope. We describe below the microcolorimeter devised by Holter-Malmstrom [28], which is shown in Fig. 59.

The light source is an ordinary microlamp (1) with a voltage stabilizer. The light beam passes through a lens system (2), falls on the silvered surface of a prism, from which it is reflected, falling (through the condenser (4) and the capillary cuvette with the solution on the microscope stage) on to the objective (5).

The device (6) is a photographic hood with a prism system, an eyepiece × 10 and a side tube for observation. On top is fixed the part (7) with the photographic element and filter. The instrument is linked to a galvanometer by a switch in part (6). The cuvette with the solvent is placed on the stage and set in position relative to the light beam; a movable prism in part (6) can be removed from the light path, a trap opened and the galvanometer set on the 100 mark. Then the cuvette with the solution is placed on the stage and the percentage passing through is measured.

Among the instruments giving a direct comparison for the analysis of small volumes, Varshavskii and Shatenshtein [103] have devised an instrument for the photographic measurement of colour intensity whose originality makes it deserving of attention.

The principle used is the following. Two capillary cuvettes, the

one filled with solvent (or a standard solution) and the other with
the solution to be examined, are set side by side in the path of a
parallel light beam immediately in front of a photographic plate,
which is set at right angles to the axis of the cuvettes. In front of
the comparison cuvette there is an optical absorber, by moving

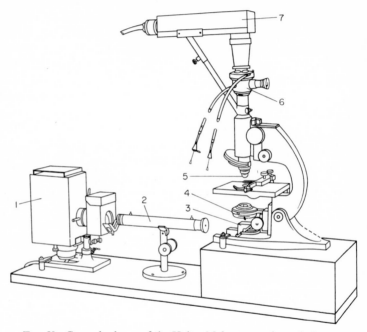

FIG. 59. General scheme of the Holter-Malmstrom microcolorimeter.

which, one can find the position corresponding to uniform blackening
of the images of the openings in the cuvettes on the exposed plate.
For an exposure the intensity of the blackening depends on the brilli-
ance of the light beam passing through the cuvette: the blackening
is less, the higher the concentration of the solution. Equal blackening from the standard solution and that under investigation, means
that the absorption by the latter is equal to the total absorption by
the standard solution and the corresponding part of the absorber.
A vernier scale serves to fix the position of the optical absorber.
A calibration curve is constructed which has as coordinates the

concentration of the solution and the position of the absorber corresponding to uniform blackening. The cuvette is then filled with the solution to be analysed, the position of the absorber for uniform blackening is determined and the concentration of the solution found from the graph. A general view of the instrument is shown in Fig. 60. A plate 2 with a tube 3 on the front is fixed on

FIG. 60. Apparatus for the photographic measurement of colour intensity.

a stand 1. In the tube there is a shutter where the cuvettes and the optical absorber are placed: the latter is arranged so that it darkens only the upper, standard, cuvette. Behind the plate there are longitudinal channels holding a cassette 5 and the photographic plate. With this instrument the authors have measured quantities down to 50 λ.

The most suitable instrument for precise work with small volumes, however, is the photoelectric spectrophotometer [14]. The best spectrophotometers for ultramicroanalytical applications are the SF-4 or Beckman's, where the slit is so arranged that its width can be altered, its effective width over the greater part of the spectrum being 1 μ. Another important feature of this type is that the cuvette holder can easily be changed.

The principal adaptation required for work with small cuvettes is, fundamentally, the construction of a suitable holder, to which, therefore, a considerable amount of study has been devoted. The

II

authors do not describe various types of holder in detail but recommend the original studies [14, 97, 104, 105] to the reader's attention.

One of the critical operations in work with capillary cuvettes is when they are being set up in the apparatus.

The light beam entering the cuvette chamber must be strictly parallel to the optical axis and fall exactly on the photoelement. The adjustment is made by changing the position of the concave mirror in the box containing the light source, after the holder with the cuvettes has been placed in the instrument. Between the light source and the capillary cuvette there is a diaphragm (of cardboard or metal): the object of this is to ensure that light on the photoelement passes through the cuvette and not under or over it. Next, the cuvette holder must be placed correctly in relation to the light beam. The holder is adjustable both in the horizontal and in the vertical direction. The lateral adjustment allows the capillary to be positioned exactly in the centre of the light beam; the vertical is necessary to ensure that the entrance windows of both cuvettes are equally illuminated. These adjustments are made with the smallest diameter cuvettes available; in this case, there will be no need for fresh adjustment if other cuvettes are used. The horizontal setting is made first, each of the cuvettes being adjusted independently until the maximum amount of light is let through them.

The correct vertical setting is found as follows. Set both cuvettes roughly at such a height in the light beam that the entrance aperture of the cuvette is opposite the aperture in the diaphragm. Then open the photoelement shutter and find the amount of light passing through one of the cuvettes. Then put the second cuvette in the light beam and make a similar determination. Continue to adjust the cuvettes until the amount of light passing through them is unchanged when the cuvettes are transposed: then the adjustment is correct.

The smallest volume that can be measured photometrically is determined by the ability of the photometer to measure the very small light beam passing through a capillary cuvette. To reinforce the very small beam in the Beckman spectrophotometer when small cuvettes (20λ capacity or less) are used, Kirk and his colleagues recommend the use of a photomultiplier tube [97]. The sensitivity of the photometer is significantly increased by this device and is as yet far from exhausted.

In work of this kind particular attention must be paid to the avoidance of chance contamination of the solutions, because even a 50 μ dust particle introduces a noticeable error in measurement.

The spectrophotometry of very small volumes is also possible with another method involving the use of a monochromator in conjunction with a microscope. This instrument is based on the Holter-Malmstrom microcolorimeter. It is simpler than the ordinary spectrophotometer, as adapted for use with small volumes, and

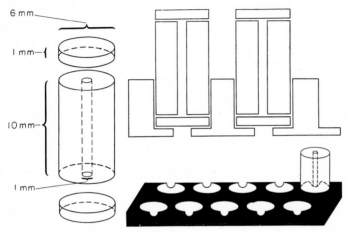

FIG. 61. Holder for microspectrophotometer cuvettes.

gives equally good results. The principle is that a very small beam of monochromatic light (the diameter of the beam is 0·4 mm) is directed from the monochromator through the capillary cuvette, which is placed in its holder on the microscope stage, and is then measured by a balanced photomultiplier with a bridge circuit.

The simplicity of construction of the cuvette holder is of interest (Fig. 61). The holder is made of Bakelite. In each of its openings a cuvette window is placed; these windows are made of polished quartz plates 6 mm in diameter and 1 mm thick. The cuvettes (capillary tubes exactly 10 mm long, 1 mm in internal and 6 mm in external diameter, with the top and bottom surfaces carefully polished flat) are placed on the windows. The cuvettes are filled from on top: a drop of solution is placed on the cuvette, which, as it drops, forces out the air, fills the cuvette and forms a capillary seal between the window below and the cuvette. The top window, which is then put on, forms a similar seal at the top. At least 30 min work may be done with such a cuvette without risk of the solution being spoiled by evaporation. The holder is placed on the microscope stage in a light-proof box with a removable lid: the cuvettes are set in in the field of view by observing through the eyepiece.

Colorimetric Ultramicrodeterminations

The procedure of making colorimetric ultramicro-determinations can be divided into three stages: (1) the preparation of the coloured solution in a quantity slightly in excess of that required to fill the cuvette (the excess is needed for the formation of the capillary seals between the cuvette surfaces and the windows); (2) the filling of the cuvette; (3) the actual measurement.

The first operation presents no difficulty to an experimentalist who has mastered the techniques of micro-investigation. The last has been described above in the section devoted to the apparatus of the colorimetric method.

It is pertinent to remark that, if visual instruments are used, it is preferable to work in the part of the spectrum where the human eye is most sensitive (yellow, orange, red colours) and, on the other hand, to avoid the blue range, because the eye has difficulty in picking up this colour in the thin layers of solution with which the ultra-microchemist is obliged to work.

CONCLUSION

THE FUTURE DEVELOPMENT OF INORGANIC ULTRAMICROANALYSIS

In the present work the fundamental and most widely used ultramicroanalytical techniques involving the use of a microscope have been described.

In the immediate future it is to be expected that the principal development will be along the lines of reducing the quantity of the substance to be analysed.

It will, obviously, be possible to observe operations performed with manipulators under the microscope by means of a television microscope [106].

In a number of cases methods of analysis in ultra-violet light will be very useful, as will be the use of the luminescent microscope: many luminescent reactions are very sensitive.

An interesting possiblity is the application of Brumberg's ultra-violet microscope [107] to the study of microcrystalline reactions. In ultraviolet rays invisible images can be made visible on a fluorescent screen. In the literature [108] the application of this method in analytical chemistry is described and its advantages compared with analysis by visible rays is demonstrated, especially in that the range of reactions used can be greatly extended.

Each year an increasing number of studies are published of work using the electron microscope, which, with magnification of 2×10^4 permits the detection of elements in the form of characteristic crystalline combinations with a sensitivity of the order of 10^{-15} to 10^{-19} g [51]. The use of the electron microscope together with new types of micromanipulators makes possible the chemical analysis of very small samples. It should be noted that, as the quantity of the substance to be analysed decreases and the dimensions of the apparatus are reduced, more importance will be attached to the development of manipulating techniques and the improvement of the various types of micromanipulator.

At the present time the problem of separating microphases from a heterogeneous substance has not been satisfactorily solved. The normal drilling is often not completely satisfactory for the purpose of ultramicroanalysis. The use of ultrasonic instruments for these purposes seems useful and possible.

One line of development is the working out of techniques and methods of determining very small quantities of impurities in the purest substances, for example, in semi-conductors, after the bulk of the macrocomponent has been removed.

It is to be expected that ultramicroanalysis will be used more for the study of radioactive substances, especially those with high specific activity.

In qualitative ultramicroanalysis, besides the identification of interesting ions, there arises the necessity of determining the physical constants characterizing the substance in question, for example, the boiling and melting points, the density and so on. This side of inorganic ultramicroanalysis is as yet little developed in comparison with the determination of the constants of small samples of organic compounds [109]. The reader will find a certain amount of information on this topic in Kirk's book [14].

It may be noted that qualitative ultramicroanalysis with the aid of the microscope is already fairly well developed, while quantitative analysis is restricted by the limited number of methods available up to the present time. Above all, the existing microbalances are not sufficiently sensitive and accurate, especially for those cases where the determination is concluded gravimetrically. In fact, research workers resort to the gravimetric method only when there is no other suitable method, or when the analysis cannot be repeated because of the extremely inadequate amount of the substance available. In such cases, after weighing, the isolated compound of the element can be preserved as a control, or can be tested for identity and purity.

The majority of the methods of quantitative analysis are founded on the measurement of some parameter functionally related to the mass. This means, principally, titrimetric and photometric methods. An important advantage of physico-chemical methods is that, when the volume of the object under investigation (liquid or gas) can be measured, or when a microsample is obtained by the selection of an aliquot of solution, the use of extremely accurate balances is not required.

Of course, in this case too the accuracy of the analysis depends largely on the instrumental error. In any case, in ultramicroanalysis just as in microanalysis, the random instrumental errors make up at least a third of the error introduced by the chemical factors [110, 111]. The physico-chemical methods with the greatest future seem to us to be the potentiometric, amperometric and coulometric, which require further development in application to the analysis of various substances. Polarographic analysis with a dropping mercury electrode is not suited to ultramicroanalysis. In this connexion it is to be expected that Kemula's polarographic method employing a stationary mercury electrode [112–114] will be developed further, for it is a very sensitive method. For the further development of the application of spectrophotometry in ultramicroanalysis, it is very important that there should be special instruments with optical systems that permit work with cuvettes of very small diameter. The construction of the cuvettes themselves is also by no means perfect as yet.

The further development of quantitative chemical ultramicro-analysis will be especially fruitful when radioactive tracers are applied: these allow the reliability of methods of separating elements to be tested by the precipitation of low solubility compounds, by extraction or ion-exchange chromatography. Another method of great promise is isotopic dilution, where the quantitative separation of the component to be determined is not required [115, 116].

REFERENCES

1. I. P. ALIMARIN and M. N. PETRIKOVA, *Zavodsk. Laboratoriya*, **24**, 29 (1958).
2. C. L. WILSON, *Chem. Age*, **66**, 543, 569 (1952).
3. A. BENEDETTI-PICHLER, *Microchem. J.*, **2**, 3 (1958).
4. J. GILLIS, *Bull. Soc. Chim. France*, **11**, C91 (1953).
5. B. CUNNINGHAM, *Discovery*, **15**, 459 (1954).
6. T. WEST, *Research*, **7**, 60 (1954).
7. R. LONGO, *Inform. quím. analit.*, **9**, 116 (1955).
8. J. GILLIS, *Experientia*, **8**, 365 (1952).
9. C. L. WILSON, *Mikrochim Acta*, 1/3, 91 (1956).
10. I. P. ALIMARIN and M. N. PETRIKOVA, *Priroda*, **1**, 81 (1955).
11. I. M. KORENMAN, *Quantitative Microchemical Analysis* (Kolichestvennyi mikrokhimicheskii analiz), Goskhimizdat, Moscow (1949).
12. *Symposium on quantitative ultramicroanalysis*, ed. by I. M. KORENMAN, Gor'kii (1949).
13. I. M. KORENMAN and YE. B. GRONSBERG, *Proc. Commission on analytical chemistry of the Acad. Sc. U.S.S.R.*, **3**(6), 150 (1951).
14. P. KIRK, *Quantitative Ultramicroanalysis* (Kolichestvennyi ul'tramikroanaliz), Foreign Lit, Publ. House, Moscow (1952).
15. A. SOBEL and A. HANOK, *Mikrochem. ver. Mikrochim. Acta*, **39**, 51 (1952).
16. R. VISWANATHAN, *Biochem. J.*, **48**, 239 (1952).
17. M. SANZ and T. BRECHBUEHLER, *Recueil trav. chim.*, **74**, 530 (1955).
18. W. PORTER and N. HOBAN, *Analyt. Chem.*, **26**, 1846 (1954).
19. R. MCDONALD, C. GERBER and A. NIELSEN, *Amer. J. Clin. Pathol.*, **25**, 1367 (1955).
20. S. BONTING and R. FEATHERSTONE, *Arch. Biochem. and Biophys.*, **61**(1), 89 (1956).
21. B. GRUNBAUM, F. SCHAFFER and P. KIRK, *Analyt. Chem.*, **25**, 480 (1953).
22. E. BISHOP, *Mikrochim. Acta*, 4/6, 619 (1956).
23. R. SCHREIBER and W. COOKE, *Analyt. Chem.*, **27**, 1475 (1955).
24. S. LORD, *Analyt. Chem.*, **24**, 209 (1952).
25. F. SADEK and H. FLASCHKA, *Angew. Chemie*, **69**, 142 (1957).
26. K. KOMAREK, *Sbor Nàrodn. musea Praze*, **11**, 33 (1955).
27. R. TANTRANON, *Analyt. Chem.*, **25**, 194 (1953).
28. G. MALMSTROM and D. GLICK, *Analyt. Chem.*, **23**, 1699 (1951).
29. K. ECKEL, *J. Biol. Chem.*, **195**, 191 (1952).
30. H. HESS and A. POPE, *J. Biol. Chem.*, **204**, 295 (1953).
31. F. SCHAFFER, J. FONG and P. KIRK, *Analyt. Chem.*, **25**, 343 (1953).
32. N. FARLOW, *Analyt. Chem.*, **29**, 883 (1957).
33. A. A. BENEDETTI-PICHLER, *The Technique of Inorganic Microanalysis* (Tekhnika neorganicheskogo mikroanaliza), Foreign Lit. Publ. House, Moscow (1951).
34. A. BENEDETTI-PICHLER, *Industr. and Engng. Chem. Analyt. Ed.*, **9**, 149, 483 (1937).

35. A. BENEDETTI-PICHLER and J. RACHELE, *Industr. and Engng. Chem. Analyt. Ed.*, **12**, 233 (1940).
36. A. BENEDETTI-PICHLER and N. CEFOLA, *Industr. and Engng. Chem. Analyt. Ed.*, **14**, 813 (1942).
37. A. BENEDETTI-PICHLER and N. CEFOLA, *Industr. and Engng. Chem. Analyt. Ed.*, **15**, 227 (1943).
38. A. LOSCALZO and A. BENEDETTI-PICHLER, *Industr. and Engng. Chem. Analyt. Ed.*, **17**, 187 (1945).
39. H. EL-BADRY and C. L. WILSON, *Mikrochem. ver. Mikrochim. Acta*, **39**, 141 (1952).
40. H. EL-BADRY and C. L. WILSON, *Mikrochem. ver. Mikrochim. Acta*, **40**, 218 (1953).
41. H. EL-BADRY and C. L. WILSON, *Mikrochem. ver. Mikrochim. Acta*, **40**, 225 (1953).
42. H. EL-BADRY and C. L. WILSON, *Mikrochem. ver. Mikrochim. Acta*, **40**, 230 (1953).
43. T. THOMPSON and C. L. WILSON, *Mikrochim. Acta*, **3/4**, 334 (1957).
44. I. P. ALIMARIN and M. N. PETRIKOVA, *Zh. analit. khimii*, **8**, 11 (1953).
45. I. P. ALIMARIN and M. N. PETRIKOVA, *Zh. analit. khimii*, **9**, 127 (1954).
46. M. N. PETRIKOVA and I. P. ALIMARIN, *Zh. analit. khimii*, **12**, 462 (1957).
47. B. TURNER, *Mikrochim. Acta*, **3**, 305 (1958).
48. I. P. ALIMARIN and M. N. PETRIKOVA, *Zh. analit. khimii*, **7**, 341 (1952).
49. J. HILLIER and R. BAKER, *J. Appl. Phys.*, **15**, 663 (1944).
50. R. BURK and O. GRUMMITT, *Recent Advances in Analytical Chemistry*, New York (1949).
51. L. I. ZEMLYANOVA and YU. M. KUSHNIR, *Zavodsk. laboratoriya*, **18**, 972 (1952).
52. R. STREBINGER and E. ORTH, *Monatsh. Chem.*, **81**, 254 (1950).
53. R. WYCKOFF, *Electron Microscopy: Technique and Application*, New York (1949).
54. I. P. ALIMARIN and M. N. PETRIKOVA, *Zh. analit. khimii*, **10**, 251 (1955).
55. J. HENSLEY, A. LONG and J. WILLARD, *Industr. and Engng. Chem.*, **41**, 1415 (1949).
56. T. BRINDLE and C. L. WILSON, *Mikrochem. ver. Mikrochim. Acta*, **39**, 310 (1952).
57. M. C. ALVAREZ-QUEROL, *Mikrochem. ver. Mikrochim. Acta*, **39**, 117 (1952).
58. P. FONBRUN, *Methods of Micromanipulation* (Metody mikromanipulyatsii), Foreign Lit. Publ. House, Moscow (1951).
59. L. OTTO, *Z. Vereines dtsch. Ingr.*, **94**, 754 (1952).
60. H. ALBER, *Mikrochemie*, **14**, 218 (1933).
61. W. PRIOR, *Nature*, **173**, C. XIX (1954).
62. L. MANHOFF and M. JOHNSON, *Science*, **112**, 2899, 76 (1950).
63. M. KOPAC, *Science*, **113**, 2931, 232 (1951).
64. G. HOEPFNER, *Lab.-Praxis*, **8**, 1 (1956).
65. J. BROWNING and L. LOCKINGEN, *Science*, **115**, 2998, 646 (1952).
66. V. BUSH, W. DURYEE and J. HASTINGS, *Rev. Sci. Instr.*, **24**, 487 (1953).
67. G. BEKESY, *Rev. Sci. Instr.*, **27**, 690 (1956).
68. I. M. KORENMAN, *Microcrystalloscopy* (Mikrokristalloskopiya), Goskhimizdat, Moscow (1952).
69. I. P. ALIMARIN and V. N. ARKHANGEL'SKAYA, *Qualitative Semi-microanalysis* (Kachestvennyi polumikroanaliz), Goskhimizdat, Moscow (1952).

70. E. CHAMOT and C. MASON, *Handbook of Chemical Microscopy*, vol. **1**, New York (1958).
71. C. DUVAL, *Traité de Micro-Analyse Minérale (Qualitative et Quantitative)*, 1/3, Paris (1954–6).
72. H. EL-BADRY, F. MCDONNEL and C. L. WILSON, *Analyt. Chim. Acta*, **4**, 440 (1950).
73. A. K. RUSANOV, *Zavodsk. laboratoriya*, **2**, 1137 (1936).
74. V. A. KALYUZHNYI, *Mineralogical symposium of the L'vov University Geological Society* (Mineralog. sb. L'vovsk. geolog. o-va pri un-te), **12**, 116 (1958).
75. M. M. KHRUSHCHOV and YE. S. BERKOVICH, *Zavodsk. laboratoriya*, **18**, 889 (1952).
76. YE. S. BERKOVICH and A. D. KURITSYNA, *Zavodsk. laboratoriya*, **15**, 868 (1949).
77. J. YOE and H. KOCH, *Trace Analysis*, New York (1957).
78. B. CUNNINGHAM and E. WERNER, *J. Amer. Chem. Soc.*, **71**, 1521 (1949).
79. B. CUNNINGHAM, *Nucleonics*, **5**, 62 (1949).
80. H. CARMICHAEL, *Canad. J. Phys.*, **30**, 524 (1952).
81. E. HESS and W. THOMAS, *Z. angew. Phys.*, **7**, 559 (1955).
82. K. BEHRNDT, *Z. angew. Phys.*, **8**, 453 (1956).
83. J. HALES and A. TURNER, *Lab. Practice*, **5**, 245, 252 (1956).
84. H. ASBURY, R. BELCHER and T. WEST, *Mikrochim. Acta*, 4/6, 598 (1956).
85. P. KIRK, R. CRAIG, J. GULLBERG and R. BOYER, *Analyt. Chem.*, **19**, 427 (1947).
86. I. M. KORENMAN, YA. N. FERTEL'MEISTER and A. P. ROSTOKIN, *Zavodsk. laboratoriya*, **16**, 800 (1950).
87. I. M. KORENMAN and YA. N. FERTEL'MEISTER, *Zavodsk. laboratoriya*, **17**, 152 (1951).
88. H. EL-BADRY and C. L. WILSON, *Royal Inst. of Chem. Monogr.*, **4**, **23** (1950).
89. H. EL-BADRY and C. WILSON, *Analyst*, **77**, 596 (1952).
90. J. MIKA, *Die Methoden der Mikromassanalyse*, Stuttgart (1958).
91. M. N. PETRIKOVA, *Zh. analit. khimii*, **14**, 239 (1959).
92. J. T. STOCK, *Analyst*, **71**, 583 (1946).
93. T. PARKS and L. LYKKEN, *Analyt. Chem.*, **22**, 1444 (1950).
94. I. P. ALIMARIN and B. I. FRID, *Zavodsk. laboratoriya*, **18**, 1300 (1952).
95. SH. ROSENBERG, J. PERRONE and P. KIRK, *Analyt. Chem.*, **22**, 1186 (1952).
96. I. P. ALIMARIN and Z. A. GALLAI, *Zavodsk. laboratoriya*, **21**, 224 (1955).
97. R. CRAIG, H. BARTEL and P. KIRK, *Rev. Sci. Instr.*, **24**, 49 (1953).
98. D. WALLACH and D. SURGENOR, *Analyt. Chem.*, **30**, 1879 (1958).
99. H. HOLTER and R. LINDERSTRØM-LANG, *Research*, **3**, 315 (1950).
100. O. KOCH, *Mikrochim. Acta*, **1**, 30 (1957).
101. J. SOMOGYI, *Z. Biol.*, **98**, 60 (1937).
102. J. SOMOGYI, *Nature*, **138**, 763 (1936).
103. YA. M. VARSHAVSKII and A. I. SHATENSHTEIN, *Zh. analit. khimii*, **13**, 294 (1958).
104. D. GLICK and B. GRUNBAUM, *Analyt. Chem.*, **29**, 1243 (1957).
105. V. EVERETT-KINSEY, *Analyt. Chem.*, **22**, 352 (1950).
106. V. ZWORYKIN, L. FLORY and R. SHRADER, *Proc. I.R.E.*, **40**, 220 (1952); *Electronics*, **25**, 150 (1952).

107. YE. M. BRUMBERG, *Dokl. Akad. Nauk S.S.S.R.*, **25,** 473 (1939); 52, 503 (1946).
108. K. P. STOLYAROV, *Zh. analit. khimii*, **7,** 195 (1952).
109. L. KOFLER and A. KOFLER, *Termo-Mikromethoden zur Kennzeichnung organischer Stoffe und Stoffgemische* (1954).
110. F. HECHT and I. DONAU, *Anorganische Mikrogewichtsanalyse*, Vienna (1940).
111. A. BENEDETTI-PICHLER, *Industr. and Engng. Chem. Analyt. Ed.*, **8,** 373 (1936).
112. W. KEMULA and Z. KUBLIK, *Analyt. Chim. Acta*, **18,** 104 (1958).
113. S. I. SINYAKOVA and SHEN' YUI-CHI, *Dokl. Akad. Nauk SSSR*, **131,** 101 (1960).
114. E. N. VINOGRADOVA and G. V. PROKHOROVA, *Zavodsk. laboratoriya*, **26,** 41 (1960).
115. I. P. ALIMARIN and G. N. BILIMOVICH, *Khim. nauka i prom.*, **1,** 74 (1956).
116. I. P. ALIMARIN and G. N. BILIMOVICH, *Intern. J. Appl. Radiation and Isotopes*, **7,** 169 (1960).

INDEX